Chemist[...]

CHALLENGE!

A CLASSROOM QUIZ GAME

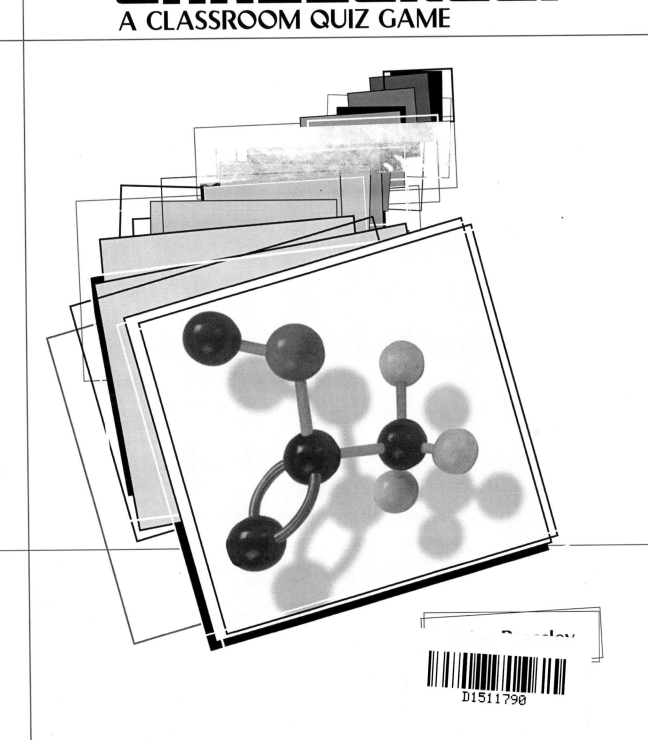

 WALCH PUBLISHING

Dedication

To my wonderful family, the excellent staffs of Fort Fairfield Middle/High School and Brunswick High School, master teachers David McCrea and Jack Despres, and, as always, to Holly.

1   2   3   4   5   6   7   8   9   10

ISBN 0-8251-4342-X

Copyright © 2002
J. Weston Walch, Publisher
P.O. Box 658 • Portland, Maine 04104-0658
www.walch.com

Printed in the United States of America

Contents

To the Teacher

Chemistry Challenge! generates real enthusiasm as it addresses the fundamentals of chemistry. It is designed to be used for several purposes: as a fun and easy way to reinforce what is being studied, as a study guide, and as a review of the unit or a culminating activity. It challenges your students to remember important facts and encourages them to enjoy themselves in the process.

The format of *Chemistry Challenge!* is similar to that of a popular television game show. A student is given the answer and is asked to provide the question. The fact given as a question is actually stated ("The SI base unit of mass"), not asked. The student response is given as a question ("What is a kilogram?"). Many students will already be familiar with the format.

The questions are classified according to general topic and further by section and category. This format lends itself to use with a variety of attention-keeping games. Some games are suggested here; you and your students may invent others.

How to Use This Book

Each section, or game, consists of five categories. Within each category are five questions, each assigned a point value of 5 through 25 depending on its relative difficulty, plus a bonus question. The bonus question is not necessarily more difficult; it may refer to an unusual fact or a less important one. It may be used in whatever way seems suitable. A point value of 5 for each bonus question would give the entire game 400 points; a value of 25 would make it a 500-point game.

These questions in this format may be used to play a variety of games. However, it may prove effective to allow the students to find the answers to, or study, the questions first. You may wish to reproduce the questions for a series of assignments and then use a game as an evaluation, a further review, or a culmination of the unit. You may find that using the questions without a game is adequate. For these reasons, the answers are presented separately at the back of the book rather than with the questions.

Feel free to modify *Chemistry Challenge!* If you have stressed something in your class that is not included in this game, it is easy to add questions. Your students will quickly learn how to make questions for you in order to extend the game. Your class can play the same game more than once, which will help them remember material more easily.

The same basic procedure can be used for playing any number of different games. Here are the directions for a typical game:

- On the board, write the categories for the game to be played along with point values for each question.

- Divide the class into teams. Play begins when one student asks for a question from a given category with a given point value. For instance, the student might say, "I want the 10-point question from the 'Atomic Structure' category."

- The game leader then reads the 10-point question from the requested category.

- Any student on the team may answer. The first person on the team to raise his or her hand is called on. (It may be the student who asked for the category to begin with.)

- If the answer is correct, record points for the team. The student who answered chooses the category and point value for the next question.

- If the answer is wrong, subtract the point value of the question from the team score. A student from the other team now has the chance to answer the question. Whoever answers the question correctly chooses the category and point value for the next question.

- If no one can answer the question, give the correct answer to the group. The student who last successfully answered a question chooses the next category and point value.

- When all the questions in the category have been used, erase the category from the board. Continue until all the categories are erased and the game is over.

Following are some other variations of the game:

Rounds

The categories and point values are displayed and the value of the bonus question is agreed upon. Bonus questions are not used until last. A scoreboard is drawn on the board to show the teams and what score they receive in each round.

The class is divided into three, four, or five groups, each having an equal number of students. (Up to 30 can play. Extra pupils may serve as scorekeepers, readers, or board keepers.) The players in each group or team sit or stand in a set order—first player, second, etc.

The game begins with Player 1 on Team 1 requesting a question. If the player responds correctly, the earned score is recorded under Team 1/Round 1. If the response is incorrect, the correct answer is read and a score of 0 is recorded. In either case, the point value is erased under the respective category. Then Player 1 of Team 2 has a turn to choose a question. After all the first players on each team have played, the play goes to the second players of each team, then the third, and so forth.

The game continues for as many complete rounds as possible. There may be several unused questions. If there are 30 players, the last player in each team chooses a category for a bonus question. Otherwise, the bonus question for each team is given to, or chosen by, the team's top scorer or chosen captain, either for that player or for the team to answer. The top-scoring team wins.

Progression

This game is set up like Rounds, preferably in five groups. The first players on each team choose a category for 5 points, the second players choose a question for 10 points, the third players go for 15, and so forth. Play continues for as many complete rounds as possible, with bonus questions handled as in Rounds.

Concentration

First, the categories and point values are written on the board and the bonus value is determined. The class is divided into two teams. The first player on one team requests a question. If the player replies correctly, his or her team gets the points, and the point value is erased below the respective category. If the player does not answer correctly, the response is announced to be wrong and nothing is erased from the board. The first person on the opposite team then chooses a question. The play goes from team to team, with each person choosing a question still listed on the board. The advantage goes to the person who knows the answer to a previously asked question and can remember where it is located on the board. Play continues until all questions have been used. The highest-scoring team wins.

Last Chance

The class is divided into two, three, four, or five teams, with the players seated or standing in a set order. The categories and point values are displayed, and the bonus value (perhaps generous) is chosen. The bonus questions are not used in regular play.

Player 1 on the first team requests a question. If the player replies correctly, his or her team earns the respective points; if the reply is incorrect, the teacher tells or explains the answer. In either case, the point value under that category is erased. The play then goes to Player 1 on the second team, who requests a question. After all the first players have had a turn, the play goes to the second players on each team, then the third, and so forth.

When all the questions have been used, the scores for each team are calculated. The next player on the lowest-scoring team chooses a category for the bonus question for his or her team. The teacher reads the question and accepts only one answer from the team. (The players may confer in order to come to an agreement.) If the reply is correct, the bonus score is added to their total. Then the second-lowest-scoring team chooses a category, then the third, and the fourth, if there are that many teams. Only one bonus question is given to each team. There may be some that are not used. The winning team is that which has the highest score.

Chemistry Bee

This game is played like a spelling bee, but no one is eliminated. First the categories and point values are displayed, and the value of the bonus question is determined. The class is divided into two teams. The first person on one team asks for a question by stating a category and point value. If the player responds correctly, his or her team receives the points and that point value is erased under that category. The next turn is taken by the first player on the other team, who chooses a question. However, if the first player's response is not correct, the same question is repeated for the first player on the other team. If the player replies correctly, his or her team gets the points and the play then goes to the second player of the first team. The play continues from one side to the other, with points going to the teams that answer correctly and the respective category points being erased from the board. The game is over when all 30 questions have been used. The team accumulating the most points wins.

No matter how you use *Chemistry Challenge!* it is an entertaining and stimulating way to review, and it's an excellent change-of-pace activity. You'll find your students eager to play it again and again.

UNIT 1

Introductory Material

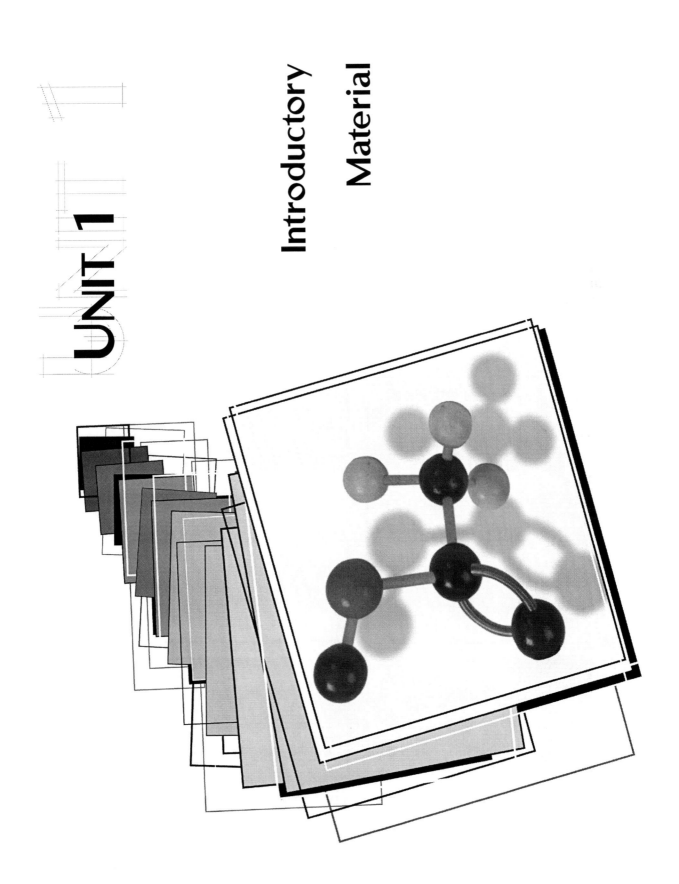

	PROBLEM SOLVING	CHEMISTRY AS A SCIENCE	SI UNITS	SI PREFIXES	SI LENGTH CONVERSIONS
5	The first item to be identified in problem solving	The collection of information to advance knowledge	The SI base unit of length	This prefix means one thousand.	The number of centimeters in a meter
10	These are carried out to collect information.	The practical application of knowledge to everyday life	The SI base unit of mass	This prefix means one tenth.	The number of millimeters in a centimeter
15	The information collected during experimentation	The branch of chemistry involving the study of carbon-based compounds	The SI base unit of time	This prefix means one hundredth.	The number of meters in a kilometer

The number of millimeters in a meter	The number of millimeters in a decimeter	The number of millimeters in a kilometer
This prefix means one thousandth.	This prefix means one millionth.	This prefix means one billionth.
The SI base unit for amount of matter	The SI base unit for temperature	The SI base unit for electrical current
The branch of chemistry that uses physics to explain the behavior of substances	The branch of chemistry concerned with identifying substances and analyzing their chemical composition	The branch of chemistry that uses chemical analysis to resolve legal issues
An educated guess, based on observed facts	The explanation of facts that have been observed over a long period of time	A statement of fact meant to explain observations unvarying over time and accepted as universal

20

25

B O N U S

N O T E S

Introductory Material
Section 2

DERIVED UNITS	COMMON NON-SI UNITS	MEASUREMENT	SIGNIFICANT DIGITS	SCIENTIFIC NOTATION
SI unit of area	The metric unit of volume	How close an answer is to an accepted value	The number of significant digits in the number 1.8	The following number expressed in scientific notation: 6 001
SI unit of volume	The metric unit of density in mass over volume	The reproducibility of a measurement	The number of significant digits in the number 6.0	The following number expressed in scientific notation: 14.2
SI unit of density	The metric unit of temperature	The digits that describe the precision of a measurement plus the final, uncertain digit	The number of significant digits in the number 10.1	The following number expressed in standard form: 1.16×10^3

5

10

15

The following number expressed in scientific notation: 82	The following number expressed in scientific notation: 0.000 43	The following number expressed in scientific notation: 2	
The number of significant digits in the number 0.023	The number of significant digits in the number 100.1	The number of significant digits in the number 200.400	
The difference between a measured value and true value without regard to sign	The amount by which a measured value differs from the true value, expressed as a percent	The most probable value of a measurement based on accepted references	
The metric unit of pressure	The metric unit of energy	The English unit of temperature	
SI unit of pressure	SI unit of energy	SI unit of concentration	
20	**25**	B O N U S	N O T E S

Introductory Material
Section 3

MATTER	COMBINATIONS OF MATTER	PROPERTIES OF MATTER I	PROPERTIES OF MATTER II	PROPERTIES OF MATTER III
5 A measure of the amount of matter in an object	It consists of two or more substances that are not chemically combined.	The physical state of a substance	Those properties that can be determined without changing the chemical makeup of a substance	The highest temperature at which it is still possible to liquefy a gas by increasing pressure
10 All matter in the universe takes up space and has this.	A kind of mixture that is the same throughout	The physical state of a substance in which volume and shape are fixed	Those properties that can be determined only by changing the chemical makeup of a substance	The pressure required to liquefy a gas at its critical temperature
15 One kind of matter with a unique set of properties	A kind of mixture that is not the same throughout	The physical state of a substance in which volume is fixed but shape is not	The kind of change in which no new substances are formed	The wearing away of metals

This mixture of usually high-temperature particles includes free electrons, protons, and neutral particles in a gaseous collection.

Of the following, the one that is a chemical change: cutting down a tree, crushing a soda can, burning a pile of leaves, or breaking a glass

Of the following, the one that is only a physical change: burning a candle, photosynthesis, digesting food, or melting an ice cube

The kind of change in which one or more new substances are formed

Those properties of a substance that do not depend on sample size

Those properties of a substance that depend on sample size

The physical state of a substance where neither shape nor volume are fixed

Another name for the gaseous state of matter

The so-called fourth state of matter

Of the following, the one that is a homogeneous mixture: salt, water, salt water, or fruit salad

Of the following, the one that is a heterogeneous mixture: salt, water, salt water, or fruit salad

A combination of two or more chemically combined substances

A substance made of one kind of atom

Of the following, the one that is an element: water, alcohol, oxygen, or salt

Of the following, the one that is a substance: salad, water, chocolate chip cookies, iced tea, or soap

20

25

B O N U S

N O T E S

Introductory Material

Section 4

	ELEMENTS AND THEIR SYMBOLS I	ELEMENTS AND THEIR SYMBOLS II	ELEMENTS AND THEIR SYMBOLS III	ELEMENTS AND THEIR SYMBOLS IV
DENSITY				
	The symbol for hydrogen	The symbol for aluminum	The symbol for lithium	The symbol for argon
5	The traditional label for solid density			
	The symbol for silicon	The symbol for zinc	The symbol for beryllium	The symbol for iron
10	The traditional label for liquid density			
	The symbol for arsenic	The symbol for mercury	The symbol for silver	The symbol for barium
15	The density formula, solved for mass			

The symbol for radon

The symbol for molybdenum

The element with the symbol In

The element with the symbol Sb

The element with the symbol Np

The element with the symbol Re

The symbol for gallium

The element with the symbol Sc

The element with the symbol Nb

The symbol for radium

The element with the symbol At

The element with the symbol La

The density formula, solved for volume

Of the following, the one with the greatest density: ice, water, or steam

Of the following, the one with the greatest density: water, iron, mercury, or gold

20

25

B O N U S

N O T E S

Introductory Material

Section 5

Elements and Their Symbols V	Elements and Their Symbols VI	Elements and Their Symbols VII	Elements and Their Symbols VIII	Elements and Their Symbols IX
The symbol for sodium	The symbol for helium	The symbol for fluorine	The symbol for boron	The symbol for carbon
The symbol for manganese	The symbol for sulfur	The symbol for potassium	The symbol for phosphorus	The symbol for nickel
The symbol for bismuth	The symbol for iodine	The symbol for xenon	The symbol for cadmium	The symbol for cesium

5

10

15

The symbol for uranium

The symbol for zirconium

The symbol for plutonium

The symbol for germanium

The symbol for rubidium

The element with the symbol Os

The element with the symbol Lr

The element with the symbol Fr

The element with the symbol Po

The element with the symbol Tc

The element with the symbol Ru

The element with the symbol Rh

The element with the symbol Es

The element with the symbol Th

The element with the symbol Gd

20

25

B O N U S

N O T E S

Introductory Material

1

ELEMENTS AND THEIR SYMBOLS X	ELEMENTS AND THEIR SYMBOLS XI	ELEMENTS AND THEIR SYMBOLS XII	ELEMENTS AND THEIR SYMBOLS XIII	ELEMENTS AND THEIR SYMBOLS XIV
The symbol for chlorine	The symbol for magnesium	The symbol for neon	The symbol for nitrogen	The symbol for oxygen
The symbol for copper	The symbol for cobalt	The symbol for chromium	The symbol for calcium	The symbol for bromine
The symbol for gold	The symbol for iridium	The symbol for krypton	The symbol for lead	The symbol for platinum

5

10

15

20	25	BONUS	NOTES
The symbol for strontium	The element with the symbol Y	The element with the symbol Am	
The symbol for selenium	The element with the symbol Yb	The element with the symbol Ac	
The symbol for tin	The element with the symbol V	The element with the symbol Cm	
The symbol for titanium	The element with the symbol Tl	The element with the symbol Pd	
The symbol for tungsten	The element with the symbol Te	The element with the symbol Pm	

Introductory Material
Section 7

1

ENERGY	FORMS OF ENERGY	REACTION ENERGY	ENERGY AND TEMPERATURE	HEAT
When a force moves an object through a distance	The kind of energy found in an alkaline battery	A chemical reaction that absorbs energy	This scale has zero as the freezing point of water.	The amount of energy needed to raise the temperature of one gram of substance one degree Celsius (or kelvin)
That energy attributed to a particle in motion	One kind of energy released from a fire	A chemical reaction that releases energy	This scale has zero as the lowest temperature possible.	In the formula $Q = mc\Delta t$, what m stands for
The energy often referred to as stored energy	The kind of energy that runs a lightbulb	The minimum amount of energy needed to start a reaction	Specific name for the lowest possible temperature on the Kelvin scale	In the formula $Q = mc\Delta t$, what Q stands for

5

10

15

In the formula $Q = mc\Delta t$, what Δt stands for	In the formula $Q = mc\Delta t$, what c stands for	The value in J/g°C or cal/g°C for the specific heat of water	
A device for measuring the heat content of a sample	This form of energy moves only from "hot" objects to "cold" objects.	A measure of the average kinetic energy of the particles in a substance	
The SI unit for measuring energy	The metric unit that is used for measuring energy, often used for measuring the amount of energy in food	The amount of energy needed to raise the temperature of one pound of water one degree Fahrenheit	
The kind of energy found in a fission reactor	The kind of energy found in the use of a lever	A kind of energy found in the human body	
The SI unit of energy	The statement that energy is conserved in any reaction	The sum of potential and kinetic energy in an object	
20	**25**	B O N U S	N O T E S

UNIT 2

Atoms and Ions

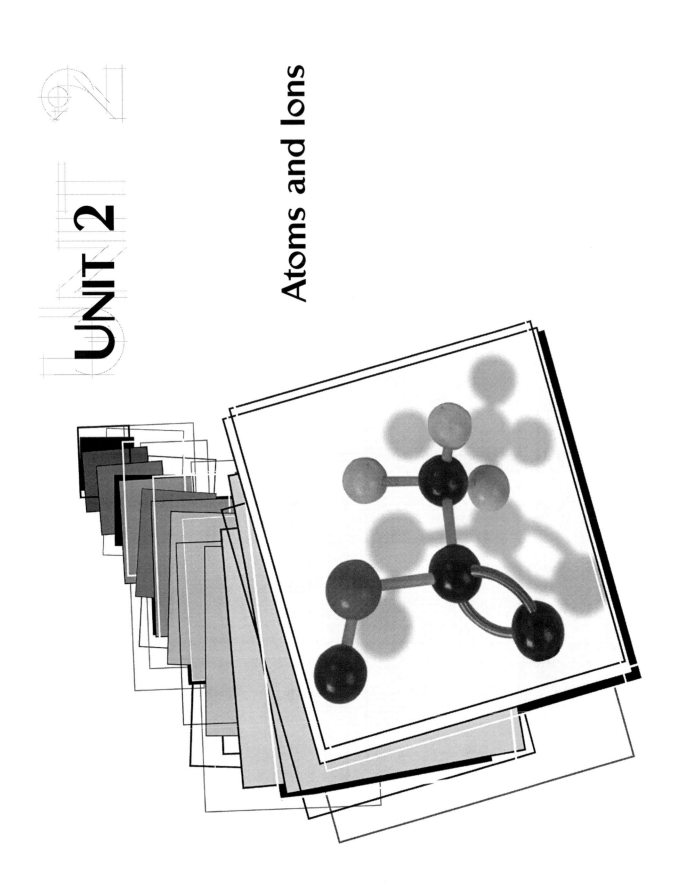

Atoms and Ions
Section 8

2

	ATOMIC STRUCTURE	DEVELOPMENT OF ATOMIC THEORY	MASS AND CHARGE	CHEMISTS AND THE ATOM	MODELS
5	The smallest sample of an element	The view that matter can be infinitely divided into smaller parts	The charge on an electron	This scientist is credited with the discovery of cathode rays.	J.J. Thomson's model of the atom
10	The subatomic particle that has a negative charge	The view that there is a smallest particle of matter that cannot be divided	The charge on a proton	This scientist is credited with the discovery of the electron.	In this model the electrons move in a fixed path around the nucleus.
15	The subatomic particle that has a positive charge	The idea that when elements form a compound, they always react in a specific proportion by mass	The charge on a neutron	This scientist is credited with discovering protons, which he initially referred to as hydrogen nuclei.	In this model the electrons are scattered in a cloud around the nucleus.

A picture or representation that helps people envision objects that are too big or too small to observe easily

The idea that it is impossible to know both the location and the velocity of a subatomic particle

In the quantum mechanical model, the smallest area where electrons are found

This scientist is best known for the law of multiple proportions.

This scientist is best known for calculating the charge on an electron.

The name of the ratio that J.J. Thomson calculated that allowed another scientist to determine the charge on an electron

The mass of an electron in kg

The mass of a proton in kg

The mass of a neutron in kg

The idea that elements combine in simple, whole-number ratios in compounds

The idea that matter is neither gained nor lost in a chemical reaction

The English chemist who first proposed the law of multiple proportions

The subatomic particle that has no charge

The central portion of an atom that contains the protons and neutrons

Particles thought to make up neutrons and protons

20

25

B O N U S

N O T E S

Atoms and Ions
Section 9

	THE NATURE OF LIGHT	LIGHT ENERGY	ATOMIC MEASUREMENTS	CHEMICAL FORMULAS I	CHEMICAL FORMULAS II
5	The fundamental units of energy that make up light	In the formula $E = hf$, what f represents	The way elements are ordered on the periodic table	This is the abbreviated form of an element's name.	A model or drawing of the way atoms are connected in a molecule
10	The distance between the peaks of two consecutive crests in a wave	In the formula $E = hf$, what E represents	Elements that have the same number of protons, but different numbers of neutrons	This is a combination of numbers and chemical symbols used as an abbreviation for a compound.	A form of analysis used to determine which elements are in a substance
15	The number of waves that pass a point in one second	In the formula $E = hf$, what h represents	The weighted average of the masses of all isotopes of an element	One-atom molecules	A form of analysis used to determine the exact amount of each element in a substance

2

Of the following, the one that is an empirical formula: CH, C_4H_4, or $C_{12}H_{12}$	Of the following, the one that is the molecular formula for hydrogen peroxide: HO, H_3O_3, H_2O_2, or H_4O_4	A chemical combination of two or more atoms
Two-atom molecules	A representation of the number of atoms of each element in one molecule of a substance	The simplest whole-number ratio of each kind of atom in one molecule of a substance
The standard isotope by which the masses of all other elements are determined	The sum of the number of protons and neutrons in an element	The mass of 1/12 of a carbon-12 atom
The value of h	The value of c in the formula $c = f\lambda$	What the symbol λ represents
The ratio of distance over time that gives the speed of a wave	The complete rainbow of light that a prism produces from white light	A unique set of individual lines of light emitted when an element is burned
20	**25**	**B O N U S**

N O T E S

2

Oxidation Numbers/ Charges I	Oxidation Numbers/ Charges II	Oxidation Numbers/ Charges III	Oxidation Numbers/ Charges IV	Oxidation Numbers/ Charges V
The charge for manganese III	The charge for chromium II	The charge for cobalt II	The charge for copper II	The charge for tungsten II
The charge for magnesium	The charge for tin II	The charge for copper I	The charge for cerium IV	The charge for antimony V
The charge for lithium	The charge for cesium	The charge for iridium IV	The charge for mercury I	The charge for silver

5

10

15

The charge for bromide

The charge for hydronium

The charge for boron

The charge for nitride

The charge for sulfide

The charge for hydrogen sulfate

The charge for hydrogen carbonate

The charge for chlorite

The charge for ammonium

The charge for chlorate

The charge for permanganate

The charge for thiosulfate

The charge for azide

The charge for hypochlorite

The charge for iodate

20

25

B O N U S

N O T E S

Atoms and Ions
Section 11

OXIDATION NUMBERS/ CHARGES VI	OXIDATION NUMBERS/ CHARGES VII	OXIDATION NUMBERS/ CHARGES VIII	OXIDATION NUMBERS/ CHARGES IX	OXIDATION NUMBERS/ CHARGES X
The charge for cerium III	The charge for zirconium II	The charge for cobalt III	The charge for iridium II	The charge for iron II
The charge for phosphorus V	The charge for germanium IV	The charge for rhodium III	The charge for thallium III	The charge for mercury II
The charge for tin IV	The charge for potassium	The charge for rubidium	The charge for hydrogen	The charge for indium

5

10

15

The charge for zinc

The charge for sulfite

The charge for tartrate

The charge for aluminum

The charge for hydrogen sulfide

The charge for formate

The charge for calcium

The charge for sulfate

The charge for arsenate

The charge for phosphide

The charge for carbide

The charge for cyanide

The charge for fluoride

The charge for carbonate

The charge for molybdate

20

25

B O N U S

N O T E S

Atoms and Ions
Section 12

OXIDATION NUMBERS / CHARGES XI	OXIDATION NUMBERS / CHARGES XII	OXIDATION NUMBERS / CHARGES XIII	OXIDATION NUMBERS / CHARGES XIV	OXIDATION NUMBERS / CHARGES XV
The charge for vanadium II	The charge for strontium II	The charge for chromium III	The charge for antimony III	The charge for iron III
The charge for phosphorus III	The charge for titanium III	The charge for nickel II	The charge for platinum II	The charge for uranium III
The charge for thorium IV	The charge for lead IV	The charge for titanium IV	The charge for tungsten IV	The charge for tungsten V

5

10

15

20			
The charge for iodide	The charge for beryllium	The charge for hydride	The charge for thallium	The charge for sodium

25			
The charge for benzoate	The charge for nitrite	The charge for phosphate	The charge for phosphite	The charge for hydrogen sulfite

B O N U S			
The charge for periodate	The charge for perchlorate	The charge for chromate	The charge for borate	The charge for dichromate

N O T E S

Atoms and Ions
Section 13

2

Oxidation Numbers / Charges XVI	Oxidation Numbers / Charges XVII	Oxidation Numbers / Charges XVIII	Oxidation Numbers / Charges XIX	Oxidation Numbers / Charges XX
The charge for lead II	The charge for bismuth III	The charge for gallium III	The charge for iridium III	The charge for indium III
The charge for vanadium III	The charge for manganese II	The charge for uranium IV	The charge for vanadium IV	The charge for bismuth V
The charge for uranium V	The charge for vanadium V	The charge for platinum IV	The charge for zirconium IV	The charge for rubidium

5

10

15

The charge for chloride

The charge for barium

The charge for cadmium

The charge for selenide

The charge for oxide

The charge for nitrate

The charge for hydroxide

The charge for bromate

The charge for acetate

The charge for peroxide

The charge for oxalate

The charge for selenate

The charge for silicate

The charge for hydrogen phosphate

The charge for hexafluorosilicate

20

25

B O N U S

N O T E S

UNIT 3

Compounds

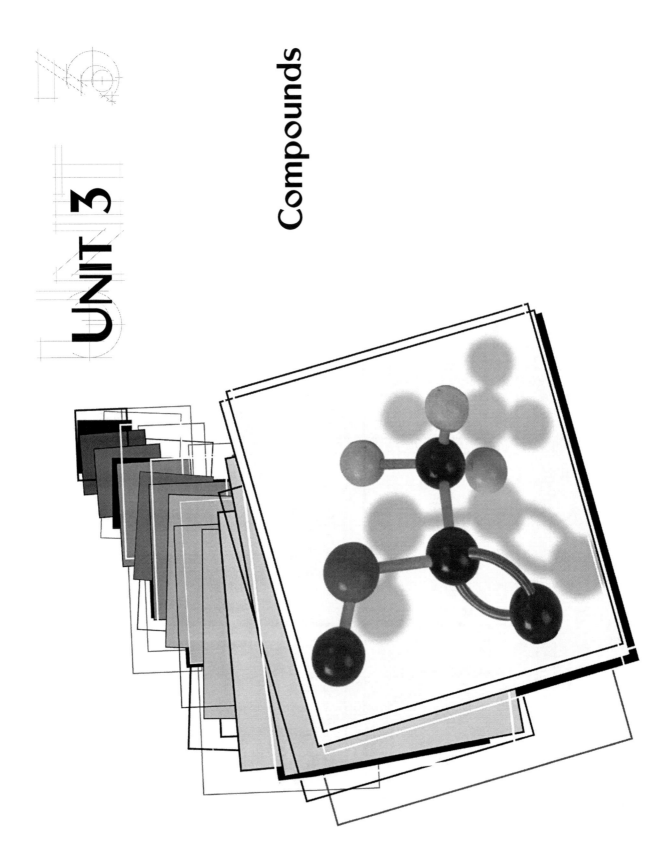

Compounds
Section 14

3

COMPOUNDS I	COMPOUNDS II	COMPOUNDS III	THE STOCK SYSTEM	MOLECULAR PREFIXES
These elements are on the left side of the periodic table and conduct electricity.	Three-dimensional repeating arrangement of atoms, molecules, or ions in a solid	This is the smallest unit of an ionic compound	Acids that are water solutions of binary hydrogen compounds	The molecular prefix for the number 1
These elements are on the right side of the periodic table and are poor conductors of electricity.	The pattern formed by all of the crystals in a solid	A compound formed from only two elements	Acids that are water solutions of ternary hydrogen compounds	The molecular prefix for the number 3
Particles with positive or negative charges	A solid formed when covalent bonds create a repeating crystal pattern	A group of two or more atoms sharing a collective charge	The prefix on a ternary acid with the lowest possible number of oxygen atoms	The molecular prefix for the number 4

5

10

15

The molecular prefix for the number 6	The molecular prefix for the number 8	The molecular prefix for the number 9	
The prefix on a ternary acid with the highest possible number of oxygen atoms	The oxidation number of Cl in hypochlorous acid, HClO	The oxidation number of Cl in perchloric acid, HClO$_4$	
A compound formed from only three elements	Compounds made of molecules	The convention for expressing the apparent charge of an ion	
Elements that have some properties of both metals and nonmetals	A compound in which the individual bonds are formed by the transfer of electrons	A compound in which the individual bonds are formed by sharing electrons	
Compounds formed when positive and negative particles are drawn together	Ions with a positive charge	Ions with a negative charge	
20	**25**	B O N U S	N O T E S

Compounds
Section 15

NAMES AND FORMULAS I	NAMES AND FORMULAS II	NAMES AND FORMULAS III	NAMES AND FORMULAS IV	NAMES AND FORMULAS V
This compound has the formula CuO.	This compound has the formula SO_3.	This compound has the formula Al_2O_3.	This compound has the formula Al_2S_3.	This compound has the formula Zn_3N_2.
This compound has the formula HCl.	This compound has the formula P_2I_3.	This compound has the formula Ir_3O_6.	This compound has the formula ON_3.	This compound has the formula K_2O.
This compound has the formula $Sr(CN)_2$.	This compound has the formula $BeClO$.	This compound has the formula $PtPO_3$.	This compound has the formula $BeCrO_4$.	This compound has the formula $Pt(SiF_6)_2$.

5

10

15

3

The formula for the compound dinitrogen tetrabromide	The formula for the compound ammonium nitrate	The formula for the compound copper (I) oxide	
The formula for the compound trisulfur disulfide	The formula for the compound lithium cyanide	The formula for the compound cobalt (II) arsenate	
The formula for the compound dinitrogen monoxide	The formula for the compound hydrogen sulfide	The formula for the compound chromium (III) bromide	
The formula for the compound trisulfur hexafluoride	The formula for the compound sodium sulfate	The formula for the compound tin (IV) oxide	
The formula for the compound dicarbon trisulfide	The formula for the compound ammonium chromate	The formula for the compound carbon (II) oxide	
20	**25**	B O N U S	N O T E S

Compounds
Section 16

NAMES AND FORMULAS VI	NAMES AND FORMULAS VII	NAMES AND FORMULAS VIII	NAMES AND FORMULAS IX	NAMES AND FORMULAS X
This compound has the formula $AlCl_3$.	This compound has the formula SrO_2.	This compound has the formula AlF_3.	This compound has the formula SO_2.	This compound has the formula $BeBr$.
This compound has the formula OF_2.	This compound has the formula LiI.	This compound has the formula O_4F_2.	This compound has the formula $MgCl_2$.	This compound has the formula NO_3.
This compound has the formula $Ca(BrO_3)_2$.	This compound has the formula $Pb_3(PO_4)_4$.	This compound has the formula $Ca(OH)_2$.	This compound has the formula $NiAsO_4$.	This compound has the formula $Co_2(C_2O_4)_3$.

5

10

15

3

The formula for the compound triphosphorus monoxide	The formula for the compound dinitrogen tetrafluoride	The formula for the compound triphosphorus dioxide	The formula for the compound dinitrogen trioxide	The formula for the compound tetraphosphorus decoxide
The formula for the compound sodium selenide	The formula for the compound hydrogen oxide	The formula for the compound barium permanganate	The formula for the compound lithium sulfite	The formula for the compound hydrogen chloride
The formula for the compound gallium (III) chloride	The formula for the compound iridium (III) oxide	The formula for the compound iron (III) cyanide	The formula for the compound lead (II) bromate	The formula for the compound manganese (II) perchlorate

20

25

B O N U S

N O T E S

Compounds
Section 17

NAMES AND FORMULAS XI	NAMES AND FORMULAS XII	NAMES AND FORMULAS XIII	NAMES AND FORMULAS XIV	NAMES AND FORMULAS XV
This compound has the formula SnS.	This compound has the formula CBr_4.	This compound has the formula $SrSO_3$.	This compound has the formula CCl_3.	This compound has the formula SnO_2.
This compound has the formula MgH_2.	This compound has the formula NO_2.	This compound has the formula MgS.	This compound has the formula NO.	This compound has the formula $MnCl_2$.
This compound has the formula NH_4NO_2.	This compound has the formula $Cr(NO_3)_2$.	This compound has the formula Na_3PO_4.	This compound has the formula $FeSiO_3$.	This compound has the formula $KHSO_3$.

3

5

10

15

The formula for the compound carbon dioxide

The formula for the compound magnesium chloride

The formula for the compound thorium (IV) iodide

The formula for the compound phosphorus trichloride

The formula for the compound sodium oxalate

The formula for the compound silicon (IV) chloride

The formula for the compound oxygen difluoride

The formula for the compound beryllium arsenate

The formula for the compound platinum (II) fluoride

The formula for the compound tetranitrogen trichloride

The formula for the compound magnesium carbonate

The formula for the compound nitrogen (IV) oxide

The formula for the compound dinitrogen trisulfide

The formula for the compound sodium oxide

The formula for the compound mercury (II) hydrogen phosphate

20

25

B O N U S

N O T E S

Compounds
Section 18

3

NAMES AND FORMULAS XVI	NAMES AND FORMULAS XVII	NAMES AND FORMULAS XVIII	NAMES AND FORMULAS XIX	NAMES AND FORMULAS XX
This compound has the formula CCl_4.	This compound has the formula SI_2.	This compound has the formula CF_4.	This compound has the formula S_3Br_4.	This compound has the formula CO.
This compound has the formula NCl_3.	This compound has the formula N_2Cl_3.	This compound has the formula Na_2S.	This compound has the formula $NaCl$.	This compound has the formula N_2Cl_5.
This compound has the formula $Mn(CN)_3$.	This compound has the formula $Ca(HSO_4)_2$.	This compound has the formula $Fe(ClO_3)_3$.	This compound has the formula $Ir(C_2H_3O_2)_2$.	This compound has the formula $Ca_3(PO_4)_2$.

5

10

15

The formula for the compound nitrogen monoxide

The formula for the compound carbon tetrafluoride

The formula for the compound carbon tetrachloride

The formula for the compound tetranitrogen monoiodide

The formula for the compound nitrogen trisulfide

The formula for the compound magnesium sulfide

The formula for the compound potassium phosphate

The formula for the compound calcium phosphate

The formula for the compound potassium chromate

The formula for the compound beryllium cyanide

The formula for the compound lead (II) hydroxide

The formula for the compound iron (III) nitrite

The formula for the compound gallium (III) chlorate

The formula for the compound cobalt (II) hydrogen carbonate

The formula for the compound chromium (II) fluoride

20

25

B O N U S

N O T E S

Compounds
Section 19

NAMES AND FORMULAS XXI	NAMES AND FORMULAS XXII	NAMES AND FORMULAS XXIII	NAMES AND FORMULAS XXIV	NAMES AND FORMULAS XXV
This compound has the formula PO_3.	This compound has the formula $CrBr_3$.	This compound has the formula PF_5.	This compound has the formula Cu_2S.	This compound has the formula PCl_5.
This compound has the formula Na_2O.	This compound has the formula N_2I.	This compound has the formula N_3O.	This compound has the formula N_2O.	This compound has the formula N_3I_4.
This compound has the formula $MgCO_3$.	This compound has the formula Li_2CO_3.	This compound has the formula Na_2SO_4.	This compound has the formula $NaBrO_3$.	This compound has the formula $NiCO_3$.

3

5

10

15

Chemistry Challenge!

The formula for the compound sulfur dioxide	The formula for the compound carbon trioxide	The formula for the compound oxygen trinitride
The formula for the compound phosphorus pentachloride	The formula for the compound nitrogen triiodide	

The formula for the compound sodium hexafluorosilicate

The formula for the compound calcium phosphite

The formula for the compound potassium silicate

The formula for the compound calcium silicate

The formula for the compound rubidium sulfate

The formula for the compound mercury (I) cyanide

The formula for the compound nitrogen (V) oxide

The formula for the compound sulfur (VI) oxide

The formula for the compound chromium (III) oxalate

The formula for the compound cadmium peroxide

20

25

B O N U S

N O T E S

Compounds
Section 20

NAMES AND FORMULAS XXVI	NAMES AND FORMULAS XXVII	NAMES AND FORMULAS XXVIII	NAMES AND FORMULAS XXIX	NAMES AND FORMULAS XXX
	This compound has the formula PCl_3.	This compound has the formula CuI_2.	This compound has the formula PbO_2.	This compound has the formula Ga_2O_3.
This compound has the formula Cu_3N_2.	This compound has the formula N_2O_5.	This compound has the formula N_2S_3.	This compound has the formula $Ag_2C_2O_4$.	This compound has the formula $Zn(OH)_2$.
This compound has the formula N_2O_3.	This compound has the formula $Ni(CN)_2$.	This compound has the formula $CoSiF_6$.	This compound has the formula $(Hg_2)_3P_2$.	This compound has the formula $GaHSO_4$.
This compound has the formula $Hg_2(CN)_2$.				

5

10

15

Chemistry Challenge!

The formula for the compound aluminum iodide

The formula for the compound iridium (III) phosphate

The formula for the compound platinum (II) nitrite

The formula for the compound dioxygen trichloride

The formula for the compound aluminum carbonate

The formula for the compound nickel (II) carbonate

The formula for the compound phosphorus tetrachloride

The formula for the compound cesium hypochlorite

The formula for the compound lead (IV) oxide

The formula for the compound dioxygen pentachloride

The formula for the compound magnesium iodide

The formula for the compound iron (III) acetate

The formula for the compound disulfur pentabromide

The formula for the compound calcium tartrate

The formula for the compound copper (I) hydrogen sulfate

20

25

B O N U S

N O T E S

Chemistry Challenge! 45

Compounds
Section 21

3

NAMES AND FORMULAS XXXI	NAMES AND FORMULAS XXXII	NAMES AND FORMULAS XXXIII	NAMES AND FORMULAS XXXIV	NAMES AND FORMULAS XXXV
This compound has the formula PbO.	This compound has the formula H_2S.	This compound has the formula P_4H_{10}.	This compound has the formula HBr.	This compound has the formula P_2O_5.
This compound has the formula $Al(MnO_4)_3$.	This compound has the formula $Th_3(AsO_4)_4$.	This compound has the formula $Al_2(Cr_2O_7)_3$.	This compound has the formula $Th(HCO_3)_4$.	This compound has the formula $Ba(NO_3)_2$.
This compound has the formula $FeC_4H_4O_6$.	This compound has the formula $Cr_2(CO_3)_3$.	This compound has the formula $CuHCO_3$.	This compound has the formula $Co(C_2H_3O_2)_2$.	This compound has the formula $Cr(ClO_2)_3$.

5

10

15

20	25	BONUS
The formula for the compound strontium hexafluorosilicate	The formula for the compound aluminum chloride	The formula for the compound thorium (IV) oxide
The formula for the compound lithium carbonate	The formula for the compound tin (IV) sulfite	The formula for the compound chromium (III) oxide
The formula for the compound ammonium chlorate	The formula for the compound cobalt (II) dichromate	The formula for the compound copper (I) sulfide
The formula for the compound sodium sulfide	The formula for the compound strontium (II) phosphate	The formula for the compound iron (III) oxide
The formula for the compound hydrogen bromide	The formula for the compound zinc hydroxide	The formula for the compound lead (II) oxide

NOTES

UNIT 4

Reactions and Gas Laws

Reactions and Gas Laws
Section 22

Note: A calculator may be needed to complete this section.

	STOICHIOMETRY	MOLE RELATIONSHIPS I	MOLE RELATIONSHIPS II	MOLE RELATIONSHIPS III	MOLE RELATIONSHIPS IV
5	The sum of the atomic masses in a chemical formula	The number of grams in one mole of carbon	The number of grams in one mole of (diatomic) oxygen gas	The number of grams in one mole of sodium	The number of grams in one mole of iron
10	The sum of the atomic masses in a molecular formula	The number of moles in 22 g of carbon	The number of moles in 48 g of (diatomic) oxygen gas	The number of moles in 99 g of sodium	The number of moles in 350 g of iron
15	The mass of an atom, numerically equal to its atomic mass, but expressed in grams	The volume in L or dm^3 of gas evolved from 2.0 moles of O$_2$ at STP	The volume in L or dm^3 of gas evolved from 4.8 moles of H$_2$O at STP	The volume in L or dm^3 of gas evolved from 1.6 moles of O$_2$ at STP	The volume in L or dm^3 of gas evolved from 0.090 moles of CO at STP

The number of atoms in 0.004 moles of iron	The volume in L or dm^3 of gas evolved from 61 g of CO at STP	The number of atoms found in 36.6 g of iron	
The number of atoms in 7 moles of sodium	The volume in L or dm^3 of gas evolved from 61 g of CO_2 at STP	The number of atoms found in 74.4 g of sodium	
The number of atoms in 2 moles of (diatomic) oxygen gas	The volume in L or dm^3 of gas evolved from 98 g of H_2O at STP	The number of atoms found in 14 g of (diatomic) oxygen gas	
The number of atoms in 1.4 moles of carbon	The volume in L or dm^3 of gas evolved from 20 g of O_2 at STP	The number of atoms found in 17 g of carbon	
The mass of a formula, numerically equal to the sum of the atomic masses, but expressed in grams	The mass of a molecule, numerically equal to the sum of the atomic masses, but expressed in grams	The numerical value of Avogadro's number	
20	**25**	B O N U S	N O T E S

Reactions and Gas Laws

Section 23

Note: A calculator may be needed to complete this section.

Mole Relationships V	Mole Relationships VI	Mole Relationships VII	Mole Relationships VIII	Mole Relationships IX
The number of grams in one mole of calcium	The number of grams in one mole of (diatomic) hydrogen gas	The number of grams in one mole of copper	The number of grams in one mole of (diatomic) bromine	The number of grams in one mole of lead
The number of moles in 58.5 g of calcium	The number of moles in 33 g of (diatomic) hydrogen gas	The number of moles in 264 g of copper	The number of moles in 922 g of (diatomic) bromine	The number of moles in 35 g of lead
The volume in L or dm^3 of gas evolved from 2.21 moles of CCl_4 at STP	The volume in L or dm^3 of gas evolved from 3.9 moles of He at STP	The volume in L or dm^3 of gas evolved from 0.228 moles of Ne at STP	The volume in L or dm^3 of gas evolved from 0.12 moles of H_2 at STP	The volume in L or dm^3 of gas evolved from 0.002 28 moles of Rn at STP

5

10

15

4

| The number of atoms in 9.9×10^{-23} moles of lead | The volume in L or dm^3 of gas evolved from 8 522 g of Rn at STP | The number of atoms found in 1.3×10^{-21} g of lead |

| The number of atoms in 1.1 moles of (diatomic) bromine | The volume in L or dm^3 of gas evolved from 66 g of H_2 at STP | The number of atoms found in 4.4×10^{-22} g of (diatomic) bromine |

| The number of atoms in 2.4×10^{-23} moles of copper | The volume in L or dm^3 of gas evolved from 228 g of Ne at STP | The number of atoms found in 1.1 g of copper |

| The number of atoms in 1.4×10^{-20} moles of (diatomic) hydrogen gas | The volume in L or dm^3 of gas evolved from 93 g of He at STP | The number of atoms found in 19.0 g of (diatomic) hydrogen gas |

| The number of atoms in 0.003 moles of calcium | The volume in L or dm^3 of gas evolved from 221 g of CCl_4 at STP | The number of atoms found in 24.2 g of calcium |

20

25

B O N U S

N O T E S

Reactions and Gas Laws
Section 24

4

	CHEMICAL EQUATIONS	CHEMICAL REACTIONS	BALANCED EQUATION RELATIONSHIPS	PHASES AND PRESSURE	PHASES AND TEMPERATURE
5	Those substances in a chemical reaction that exist before the reaction takes place	A reaction in which two simple substances combine to form a new, more complex substance	The belief that equal volumes of gas under equal conditions have an equal number of particles	Force exerted on an area	The point at which a liquid becomes a gas at a constant temperature
10	Those substances in a chemical reaction that exist after the reaction is finished	A reaction in which a complex substance is broken into two or more simple substances	The volume one mole of gas occupies at STP	That pressure exerted by the gases that surround the earth	The point at which a gas becomes a liquid at a constant temperature
15	A substance that increases the speed of a chemical reaction but is not consumed in the reaction	A reaction in which a free element becomes an ion and an ion becomes a free element	A problem in which the mass of a substance is used to calculate the mass of another substance in the same reaction	The standard temperature for STP reactions	The point at which a solid becomes a liquid at a constant temperature

The point at which a liquid becomes a solid at a constant temperature

The process by which a liquid can become a gas at varying temperatures

The process by which a gas can become a liquid at varying temperatures

The standard pressure for STP reactions

The number of pascals in a kilopascal

The derived unit that is the basis for the kPa

The name for substances that are not completely consumed in a reaction

The name for a substance in a reaction that runs out, thereby stopping the reaction

A problem in which a known volume is used to determine the volume of a second substance in the reaction

A reaction in which the cation of one substance exchanges with the cation of the other substance

An insoluble substance formed in a chemical reaction

A reaction in which an element or compound burns in oxygen

Number placed in front of each formula in a balanced chemical equation

Placing coefficients in a chemical equation to ensure that the number of each type of atom in the reactants is equal to the number in the products

A reaction that releases energy as one of the products

20

25

B O N U S

N O T E S

Reactions and Gas Laws

Section 25

	KINETIC THEORY	PHASE CHANGES I	PHASE CHANGES II	PHASE CHANGES III	POTPOURRI
5	According to the kinetic theory, the smallest particle of any gas	The pressure exerted by a liquid in equilibrium with its vapor	The separation of liquids by their differing boiling points	A kind of substance that can absorb moisture from the air	This is the number of centimeters in a meter.
10	According to the kinetic theory, all particles move in this manner.	The process by which a substance enters the liquid phase in equilibrium	The process in which a solid changes to a gas without passing through the liquid phase	A compound with the water removed	A substance made of two or more kinds of atoms chemically combined
15	According to the kinetic theory, all collisions are of this kind.	The energy needed as a unit of mass is changed from a liquid to a gas at a fixed temperature	A solid compound that contains a definite proportion of water	The name of the water trapped in a crystal	The SI unit of temperature

Chemistry Challenge!

©2002 Walch Publishing

The sum of the number of the protons and neutrons in an atom

The formula for calcium chloride

The charge for the polyatomic ion sulfate

The resistance of a liquid to flow

Of the following, the one with slowest flow: a substance with high viscosity or a substance with low viscosity

The unusual change in the density of water as it passes from the liquid to the solid phase

When a crystal is heated and the trapped water explodes the crystal to get out

The spontaneous loss of water from a hydrate at room temperature

The process by which a substance can absorb enough moisture from the atmosphere to dissolve itself

The energy needed as a unit of mass is changed from solid to liquid at a fixed temperature

The energy released as a unit of mass is changed from a liquid to a solid at a fixed temperature

The energy released as a unit of mass is changed from a gas to a liquid at a constant temperature

The attraction between particles according to the kinetic theory

All particles are in motion and, therefore, have this kind of energy, according to the kinetic theory.

A measure of the average kinetic energy of the particles in a gas

20

25

B O N U S

N O T E S

Reactions and Gas Laws
Section 26

4

BOYLE'S LAW	CHARLES'S LAW	GAY-LUSSAC'S LAW	THE COMBINED GAS LAW	THE IDEAL GAS LAW
The equation for Boyle's law	The equation for Charles's law	The equation for Gay-Lussac's law	This is the combined gas law.	This is the ideal gas equation.
The quantity represented by P in Boyle's law	The quantity represented by T in Charles's law	The formula $P_1/T_1 = P_2/T_2$, solved for P_2	The formula $P_1V_1/T_1 = P_2V_2/T_2$, solved for P_2	The quantity represented by n in the ideal gas law
The quantity represented by V in Boyle's law	The formula $V_1/T_1 = V_2/T_2$, solved for T_2	The formula $P_1/T_1 = P_2/T_2$, solved for T_2	The formula $P_1V_1/T_1 = P_2V_2/T_2$, solved for V_2	The quantity represented by R in the ideal gas law

5

10

15

The formula $PV = nRT$, solved for P

The formula $PV = nRT$, solved for T

The formula $PV = nRT$, solved for n

The formula $P_1V_1/T_1 = P_2V_2/T_2$, solved for T_2

If pressure is held constant, the combined gas law becomes this law.

If temperature is held at a constant, the combined gas law becomes this law.

The value of P_2 if the initial temperature is doubled

The value of P_2 if the initial temperature is halved

The value of T_2 if the initial pressure is doubled

The formula $V_1/T_1 = V_2/T_2$, solved for V_2

The value of T_2 if the initial volume is doubled

The value of T_2 if the initial volume is halved

The formula $P_1V_1 = P_2V_2$, solved for P_2

The value of V_2 if the initial pressure is doubled

The value of V_2 if the initial pressure is cut in half

20

25

B O N U S

N O T E S

UNIT 5

The Periodic Nature of Chemistry

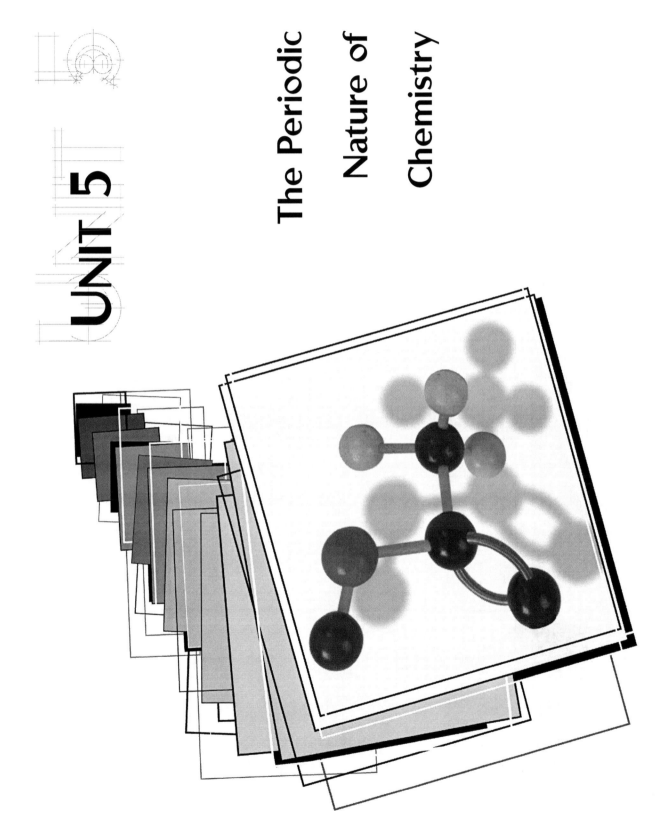

The Periodic Nature of Chemistry

Section 27

ATOMIC STRUCTURE AND ELECTRON CONFIGURATIONS I	ATOMIC STRUCTURE AND ELECTRON CONFIGURATIONS II	ELECTRON CONFIGURATIONS	PERIODIC TABLE I	PERIODIC QUANTITIES
				The counting numbers in each box on the periodic table that indicate the order of the elements
			The name for the vertical columns on the periodic table	The numbers with decimals in each box on the periodic table; elements were originally organized according to these
		The element with the configuration $1s^1$	The name for the horizontal rows on the periodic table	The full word that indicates the particular element in each box
	The state of an electron as it moves to a higher energy level within the atom	The element with the configuration $1s^2 2s^2 2p^2$	Elements toward the left of the periodic table, generally with loose outer electrons	
	The model that combines atomic orbitals in the same atom as a way to explain molecular behavior	The element with the configuration $1s^2 2s^2 2p^6$		
5 This represents the number of shells or energy levels in an atom.	The first subdivision of a principal energy level			
10	The principle that states that two electrons in the same orbital must have opposite spins			
15 The first subdivision of a sublevel, where electrons are found				

5

20

The four letters representing the four kinds of subshells in an atom

The electrons in the highest energy level of an atom

The element with the configuration $1s^2 2s^2 2p^6 3s^1$

Elements toward the top right of the periodic table, generally poor conductors of electricity

The abbreviation for an element's name

25

In increasing order, the four numbers of electrons found in the orbitals of an atom

The maximum number of valence electrons for elements 1–20

The element with the configuration $1s^2 2s^2 2p^6 3s^2 3p^5$

The elements generally found on the "staircase" between the metals and nonmetals

In some tables a more detailed expression of this type might be found: $1s^2 2s^2 2p^3$.

B O N U S

The shape of an s orbital

The two ways that valence electrons can form ionic or covalent bonds

The element with the configuration $1s^2 2s^2 2p^6 3s^2 3p^6 4s^2 3d^{10} 4p^6$

The name for elements with atomic number higher than 92

Numbers such as these, which are found in some tables: 1+, 3–

N O T E S

The Periodic Nature of Chemistry

Section 28

5

PERIODIC TABLE II	GROUP 1	GROUP 2	GROUP 17	GROUP 18
	The symbol for the element hydrogen	The symbol for the element beryllium	The symbol for the element fluorine	The symbol for the element helium
Another name for column 1, I, or IA of the periodic table	The symbol for the element lithium	The symbol for the element magnesium	The symbol for the element chlorine	The symbol for the element neon
5				
Another name for column 2, II, or IIA of the periodic table	The symbol for the element sodium	The symbol for the element calcium	The symbol for the element bromine	The symbol for the element argon
10				
Another name for column 18, VIII, or VIIIA of the periodic table				
15				

Another name for column 17, VII, or VIIA of the periodic table	The name of the element with the symbol K	The name of the element with the symbol Sr	The name of the element with the symbol I
Another name for column 16, VI, or VIA of the periodic table	The name of the element with the symbol Rb	The name of the element with the symbol Ba	The name of the element with the symbol At
Another name for column 14, IV, or IVA of the periodic table	The name of the element with the symbol Cs	The name of the element with the symbol Ra	The collective name for group 17

The name of the element with the symbol Kr

The name of the element with the symbol Xe

The name of the element with the symbol Rn

20

25

B O N U S

N O T E S

The Periodic Nature of Chemistry
Section 29

	GROUPS 13–14	GROUPS 15–16	TRANSITION ELEMENTS I	TRANSITION ELEMENTS II	INNER TRANSITION ELEMENTS
5	This element is often used in ladders and roofing materials.	This element has the symbol Bi.	This metal is magnetic and is one of the prime ingredients in many kinds of steel.	This metal is a liquid at room temperature and is sometimes used in thermometers.	This element, number 99, is named after a famous Albert.
10	This element is found in all organic chemicals.	This element has the symbol Te.	This metal is used in almost all electrical wiring.	This heavy metal is used in the production of rechargeable batteries.	This element, number 95, is used in smoke detectors.
15	This element was found in pipes and paint until its toxic nature became widely known.	This element has the symbol Po.	This metal is used in making incandescent light bulbs.	This element, whose name may have come from the Latin for shining dawn, is used in coinage and is the most malleable metal.	This element is the only naturally occurring fuel for nuclear fission.

Chemistry Challenge!

This element has long been used in the manufacture of cans.	This element is an excellent conductor of heat and electricity and is used for mirror backing.	This metal is used in coinage, is magnetic, and is *not* iron.	This synthetic element was first used in nuclear weapons.
This element accounts for over 75% of the Earth's atmosphere by mass.	This metal, used in jewelry and surgical tools, is extremely expensive.	This metal is extremely hard and is used in aircraft, spacecraft, missiles, and tank armor.	This element, number 96, is named for Marie and Pierre.
This element is found naturally in borax.	This metal is used in electroplating to give surfaces a shiny, silver appearance.	This metal is used in batteries, roofing, and for galvanizing iron.	This element was first discovered by Glenn Seaborg and his team at the University of Berkeley in California in 1950.
This element is the second most abundant in the Earth's crust and is used in the production of microchips.	The red form of this element is often found in match heads and striking surfaces.		

20

25

B O N U S

N O T E S

The Periodic Nature of Chemistry
Section 30

	PERIODICITY	BONDING	OTHER BONDS	VSEPR	OTHER BOND BEHAVIORS
5	The energy needed to remove the most loosely held electron in an atom in the gas phase	The force of attraction that holds atoms together in molecules and crystals	The type of bond formed by the sharing of electrons	VSEPR stands for this phrase.	A way to describe a molecule by averaging several Lewis structures
10	The ability of an atom, already combined with another atom, to attract electrons to itself	The type of bond formed by the transfer of electrons	Substances that contain covalent bonds	The shape of a molecule with a bond angle of 180°	Asymmetric molecules that act as if they have partial charges on opposite ends
15	Half the distance between two bonded atoms, or two atoms that are as close as can be without bonding	The arrangement of two s electrons and six p electrons in an atom	A covalent substance that contains only two kinds of elements	A three-atom shape with bond angles of ≤ 120°	Molecules where all charges are symmetrically distributed

5

The force that holds molecules together by a temporary shifting of charge	The bond formed when a hydrogen atom in a molecule acts as an exposed proton	A substance with two oppositely charged ends	
A four-atom shape with bond angles of ≤ 120°	A four-atom shape with bond angles of ≤ 109.47°	A five-atom shape with bond angles of 109.47°	
A covalent bond where one atom supplies both electrons in a bond	The bond between two atoms that share two pairs of electrons	The bond between two atoms that share three pairs of electrons	
A diagram that shows the valence electrons for an atom or ion as dots around the chemical symbol for the element	The electrons in an atom that are not valence electrons	Another term for ionic bonds	
The distance from the nucleus of an ion to its outer shell of electrons	The repulsion between kernel electrons and valence electrons	The statement that elements placed in order by atomic number show repeating periodic properties	

20	**25**	B O N U S	N O T E S

Unit 6

Solutions, Kinetics, and Acids and Bases

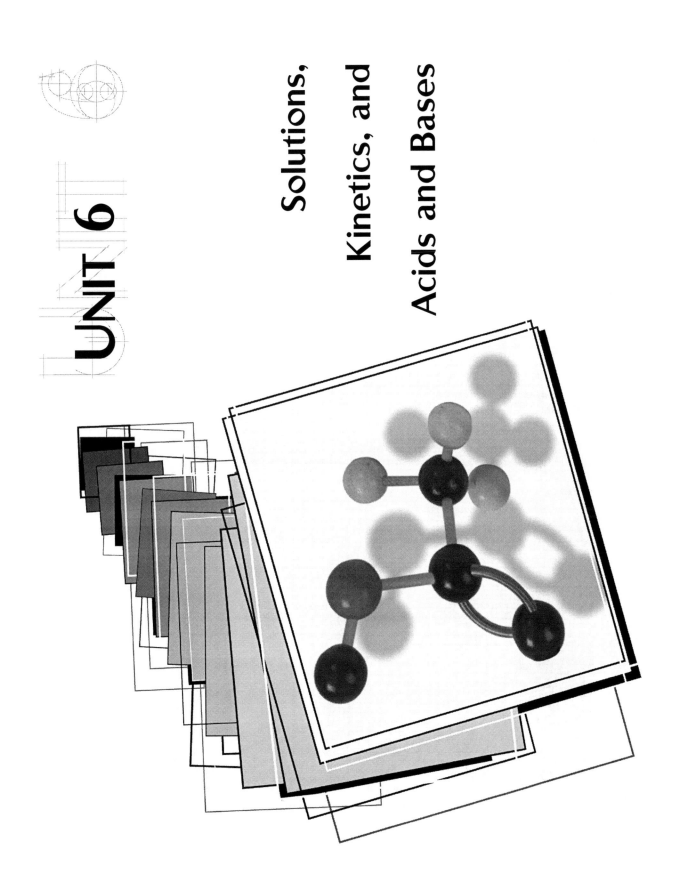

Solutions, Kinetics, and Acids and Bases

Section 31

6

	COLLIGATIVE PROPERTIES	CONCENTRATION II	CONCENTRATION I	SOLUTIONS II	SOLUTIONS I
5	Aqueous solution that conducts electricity	A measure of the moles of solute per liter (or cubic decimeter) of solution	A solution that holds all the solute it can under the given conditions	Liquids that dissolve in one another in all proportions	A mixture that is not evenly mixed throughout
10	The lowering of freezing point owing to colligative properties	A measure of the moles of solute per kilogram of solvent	A solution that holds less solute than it can under the given conditions	Liquids that do not dissolve in one another	A mixture in which all components are evenly mixed throughout
15	The raising of boiling point owing to colligative properties	The molarity if 4.4 moles of solute are dissolved in 4 liters of solution	A solution that holds more solute than it normally would under the given conditions	A solid solution containing two or more metals	That which is dissolved in a solution

In the formula $\Delta T = K_f m$, what K_f represents

The molality if 4.4 moles of solute are dissolved in 2 kg of solvent

A solution in which a large amount of solute is held relative to the amount of solvent

An alloy in which one of the metals is mercury

The part of a solution that the other part dissolves into

In the formula $\Delta T = K_b m$, what K_b represents

The number of moles of solvent used to make a 0.5 molar solution of 2 liters

A solution in which a very small amount of solute is held relative to the amount of solvent

The degree to which a substance will dissolve in a given solvent

A solution in which water is the solvent

What m represents in the formula $\Delta T = K_f m$ or $\Delta T = K_b m$

The number of moles of solvent used to make a 1.5 molal solution in 4 kg of solvent

A state in which solute dissolves at the same rate that solid precipitates out of solution

A graph that shows the amount of solute that will dissolve in a solvent across a wide range of temperatures

A solution in which alcohol is the solvent

20

25

B O N U S

N O T E S

Solutions, Kinetics, and Acids and Bases

Section 32

6

KINETICS I	KINETICS II	KINETICS III	EQUILIBRIUM	ACIDS AND BASES I
A measure of the number of moles consumed in a reaction during a given amount of time	This substance may be added to increase reaction speed, but it is not consumed in the reaction	The slowest step in a reaction mechanism	A reaction in which the reactants can be reformed readily from the products	Substances whose aqueous solutions conduct electricity
A series of steps as molecules rearrange during a chemical reaction	The principle that states a system in equilibrium will shift to reduce stress, for example, caused by a change in pressure or temperature	In thermodynamics, the name for the total of all the energy in a substance	When the forward and reverse of a reaction occur at the same rate	Substances whose aqueous solutions do not conduct electricity
Under appropriate conditions, a collision that allows reactants to become product	An insoluble substance that forms during a chemical reaction	The change in enthalpy in a chemical reaction	The kind of equilibrium found in the dissolving process in solutions	Substances whose aqueous solutions conduct electricity extremely well

5

10

15

Substances whose aqueous solutions conduct electricity only a small amount	The process by which water dissolves molecular solutes	The process by which water dissolves ionic solutes
The kind of equilibrium found in a reversible reaction	The name for K_{eq}	The terms in which K_{eq} is expressed
The heat when one mole of a substance is formed from its elements	A measure of the disorder or randomness in a system	What ΔG represents in the formula $\Delta G = \Delta H - T\Delta S$
An ion that is not changed during a chemical reaction	A short-lived particle that forms as part of a reaction's mechanism	The amount of energy required to convert reactants to product or to form an activated complex
A reaction in which all reactants are in the same phase	A reaction in which reactants may be of different phases	To speed a chemical reaction a substance may be ground into smaller pieces to increase this characteristic

20

25

B O N U S

N O T E S

Solutions, Kinetics, and Acids and Bases

Section 33

6

ACIDS AND BASES II	ACIDS AND BASES III	ACIDS AND BASES IV	ACIDS AND BASES V	ACID OR BASE?
				HCl
The name of the H_3O^+ ion	Acids neutralize these substances.	An ionic substance with a positive ion other than hydrogen and a negative ion other than hydroxide	The reaction whereby two water molecules react to form ions	
				NaOH
A substance that yields hydrogen ions (H^+) as the only positive ions	Bases neutralize these substances.	The process in which an acid and base react to form a salt and water	The negative log of the concentration of hydrogen ions in a solution	
				$NaHCO_3$
For acid ionizations, the quantity that K_a represents	Acids are known to have this kind of taste.	According to Brønsted-Lowry, an acid donates this particle.	A chemical that can make a solution resist changes to its pH	

5

10

15

©2002 Walch Publishing

H$_2$SO$_4$	HC$_2$H$_3$O$_2$	KOH	
A substance that changes color in the presence of an acid or base	A way to determine the end point of a reaction and, therefore, the quantity of reactant	Another name for the end point	
According to Brønsted-Lowry, a base accepts this particle.	A type of reaction in which a substance reacts with water	These substances can act as both an acid and a base.	
Water solutions of bases generally have this kind of taste.	Bases in aqueous solutions that conduct electricity	Bases generally turn litmus this color.	
Acids are molecular substances that ionize when added to this substance.	Chemically active metals react with acid to form this gas.	Acids often turn litmus indicators to this color.	
20	**25**	B O N U S	N O T E S

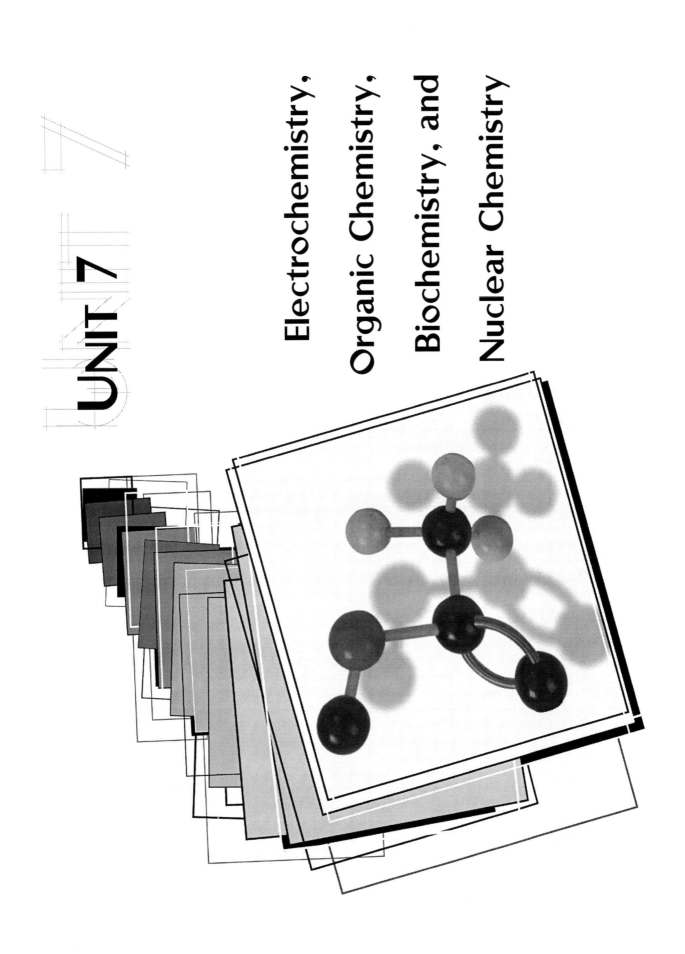

UNIT 7

Electrochemistry, Organic Chemistry, Biochemistry, and Nuclear Chemistry

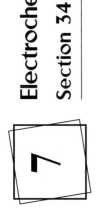

7

REDOX REACTIONS	ELECTROCHEMISTRY	ORGANIC CHEMISTRY I	ORGANIC CHEMISTRY II	ORGANIC CHEMISTRY III
A chemical reaction in which the value of the charge on an atom increases	The electrode at which reduction takes place	These substances have the same chemical formula but different structures.	A hydrocarbon in which the bonds between carbon atoms are all single, allowing the maximum number of hydrogen atoms	The members of this hydrocarbon family are all derivatives of benzene.
A chemical reaction in which the value of the charge of an atom decreases	The electrode at which oxidation takes place	These substances contain only hydrogen and carbon.	A hydrocarbon in which there may be a double bond between carbon atoms, allowing less than the maximum number of hydrogen atoms	Another name for the alkane family, it means "little affinity."
This number is also called the charge of an ion.	A substance in the dissolved or liquid phase that allows the passage of ions from one electrode to the other	Structures with a continuous chain of carbons	Hydrocarbons with only single carbon-carbon bonds	The name for any alkane that has had one hydrogen removed

5

10

15

This cyclical hydrocarbon has the formula C_6H_6.

The act of replacing one or more hydrogens in a hydrocarbon with another element or group

The act of connecting monomers into long chains

An open-chain hydrocarbon in which a double bond between at least one pair of carbon atoms is present

An open-chain hydrocarbon in which a triple bond between at least one pair of carbon atoms is present

An open-chain hydrocarbon in which double bonds exist between two pairs of carbon atoms

Structures with four or more carbons can form these chains.

Another name for a closed-chain hydrocarbon

Another name for open-chain noncyclic hydrocarbons

A concentrated solution of water and sodium chloride

The use of electrolysis to coat a material with a layer of metal

A chemical reaction brought about by an electric current

The element that causes the oxidation of another element

The element that causes the reduction of another element

A set of reactions in which the oxidation step and reduction step are written as two separate reactions

20

25

B O N U S

N O T E S

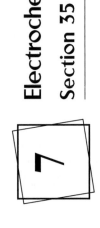

7

	ORGANIC CHEMISTRY IV	ORGANIC CHEMISTRY V	ORGANIC CHEMISTRY VI	BIOCHEMISTRY I	BIOCHEMISTRY II
5	A long-chain hydrocarbon made up of repeating pieces	This organic family contains the —CO (carbonyl) group and is known for producing fruity odors.	An alcohol in which the carbon that holds the —OH group is bonded to only one other carbon atom	The study of the chemicals that make up living things	The acids that include DNA and RNA
10	The individual pieces that make up a polymer	The members of this organic family contain the carboxyl group.	An alcohol in which the carbon that holds the —OH group is bonded to two other carbon atoms	This group contains the simple sugars.	The name abbreviated by RNA
15	The organic family in which one or more hydrogens have been replaced with an —OH group	The separation of the various organic substances by their boiling points	An alcohol in which the carbon that holds the —OH group is bonded to three other carbon atoms	This group contains the fats, waxes, and steroids.	The name abbreviated by DNA

The proper name of the —OH group	The process of breaking large organic molecules into simple molecules	Some soaps, made from carboxylic acids	This group contains what makes up a majority of muscle tissue.	A protein that acts as a catalyst for a biochemical reaction
The organic family with the general formula ROR′	An alcohol with two hydroxyl groups	Water containing many dissolved ions that interfere with detergents	The building blocks of protein	A reactant that has its reaction rate controlled by an enzyme
The organic family that contains the —CHO group	The reaction of a carboxylic acid and an alcohol forms this family of organic compounds.	The process of making soap with oils or fats and hydroxide compounds	The bond that attaches two amino acids	Monomers that become nucleic acids by polymerization

20

25

B O N U S

N O T E S

Electrochemistry, Organic Chemistry, Biochemistry, and Nuclear Chemistry

Section 36

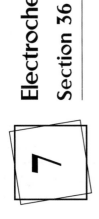

	NUCLEAR CHEMISTRY I	NUCLEAR CHEMISTRY II	NUCLEAR CHEMISTRY III	NUCLEAR CHEMISTRY IV	NUCLEAR CHEMISTRY V
5	Another name for the nuclei of helium-4	A reaction in which ^4_2He is emitted	Nuclear power plants use this fuel to produce electricity.	A specific kind of particle accelerator in which particles travel in a straight line	Einstein's famous equation that stated the mass-energy conversion relationship
10	Electrons emitted at very high speeds	One of three types of naturally occurring radiation, often written with the symbol β	A radioisotope whose movements can be followed through the human body	A specific kind of particle accelerator in which beams of particles are focused with a series of electromagnets	Those elements found after atomic number 92
15	A third type of radiation, this electromagnetic wave has the ability to penetrate even several centimeters of solid lead.	In this sort of emission, the nuclear radiation emitted takes the form of an electromagnetic wave.	The practical application of tracers in the human body	A reaction in which an atomic nucleus is split	The amount of fissionable material that will sustain a chain reaction

A moderator, often of graphite or cadmium steel	A reaction in which two light nuclei combine at high temperature to form a heavier nucleus and release enormous energy	A way to calculate the age of rocks and relics using radioactive decay	This particle has the same mass as an electron, but has a positive charge.	The time it takes for half a given sample of a radioisotope to decay
The unit of ionizing radiation used to measure the exposure of living things	The process by which a succession of nuclei are split by particles from the preceding fission	Any machine used to increase a particle's speed to allow it to be smashed and studied	Any particle that has the same mass but opposite the "normal" charge	Elements with a specified mass number and atomic number
The conversion of one element into another element by nuclear change	A substance used to slow down neutrons liberated in the fission reaction	A specific kind of particle accelerator that contains two D-shaped cells	Atoms with a nucleus of antiprotons and antineutrons orbited by positrons	An unstable nuclide that undergoes radioactive decay

20

25

B O N U S

N O T E S

Answer Key

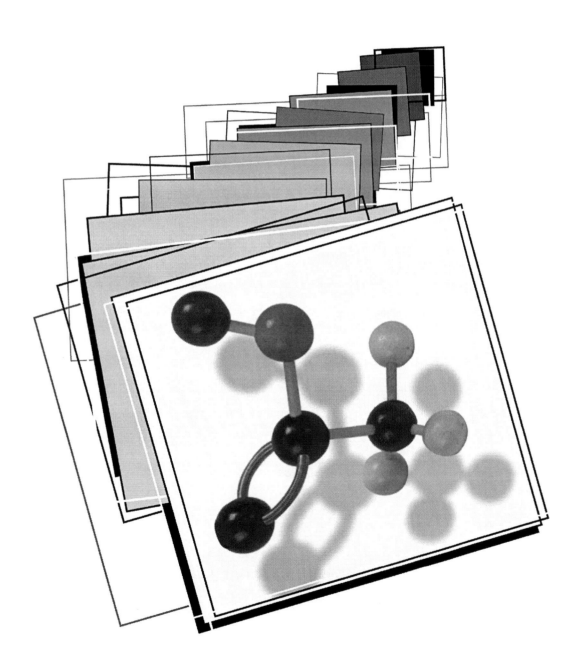

1 Introductory Material
Section 1

	Problem Solving	Chemistry as a Science	SI Units	SI Prefixes	SI Length Conversions
5	What is the problem/question?	What is pure science?	What is a meter?	What is kilo?	What is 100?
10	What are experiments?	What is technology?	What is a kilogram?	What is deci?	What is 10?
15	What is data?	What is organic chemistry?	What is a second?	What is centi?	What is 1 000?
20	What is a hypothesis?	What is physical chemistry?	What is a mole?	What is milli?	What is 1 000?
25	What is a theory?	What is analytical chemistry?	What is kelvin?	What is micro?	What is 100?
B O N U S	What is a scientific law?	What is forensic chemistry?	What is an ampere?	What is nano?	What is 1 000 000?

1 Introductory Material
Section 2

	Derived Units	Common Non-SI Units	Measurement	Significant Digits	Scientific Notation
5	What is cm^2 (m^2)?	What is a liter?	What is accuracy?	What is 2?	What is 6.001×10^3?
10	What is dm^3 (cm^3)?	What is a g/ml?	What is precision?	What is 2?	What is 1.42×10^1?
15	What is kg/m^3 (g/cm^3)?	What is Celsius?	What are significant figures?	What is 3?	What is 1 160?
20	What is a pascal?	What is mmHg (or atmospheres)?	What is absolute error?	What is 2?	What is 8.2×10^1?
25	What is a joule?	What is a calorie?	What is percent error?	What is 4?	What is 4.3×10^{-4}?
B O N U S	What is a mole/dm^3 (mole/m^3)?	What is Fahrenheit?	What is true value?	What is 6?	What is 2×10^0?

1 Introductory Material
Section 3

	Matter	Combinations of Matter	Properties of Matter I	Properties of Matter II	Properties of Matter III
5	What is mass?	What is a mixture?	What is phase?	What are physical properties?	What is the critical temperature?
10	What is mass?	What is a homogeneous mixture?	What is solid?	What are chemical properties?	What is the critical pressure?
15	What is a substance?	What is a heterogeneous mixture?	What is liquid?	What is a physical change?	What is corrosion?
20	What is an element?	What is salt water?	What is gas?	What is a chemical change?	What is plasma?
25	What is oxygen?	What is fruit salad?	What is vapor?	What are intensive properties?	What is burning a pile of leaves?
BONUS	What is water?	What is a compound?	What is plasma?	What are extensive properties?	What is melting an ice cube?

1 Introductory Material
Section 4

	Density	Elements and Their Symbols I	Elements and Their Symbols II	Elements and Their Symbols III	Elements and Their Symbols IV
5	What is g/cm^3?	What is H?	What is Al?	What is Li?	What is Ar?
10	What is g/ml?	What is Si?	What is Zn?	What is Be?	What is Fe?
15	What is m = dv?	What is As?	What is Hg?	What is Ag?	What is Ba?
20	What is v = m/d?	What is Ra?	What is Ga?	What is Mo?	What is Rn?
25	What is water?	What is astatine?	What is scandium?	What is antimony?	What is indium?
BONUS	What is gold?	What is lanthanum?	What is niobium?	What is rhenium?	What is neptunium?

1 Introductory Material
Section 5

	Elements and Their Symbols V	Elements and Their Symbols VI	Elements and Their Symbols VII	Elements and Their Symbols VIII	Elements and Their Symbols IX
5	What is Na?	What is He?	What is F?	What is B?	What is C?
10	What is Mn?	What is S?	What is K?	What is P?	What is Ni?
15	What is Bi?	What is I?	What is Xe?	What is Cd?	What is Cs?
20	What is Rb?	What is Ge?	What is Pu?	What is Zr?	What is U?
25	What is technetium?	What is polonium?	What is francium?	What is lawrencium?	What is osmium?
B O N U S	What is gadolinium?	What is thorium?	What is einsteinium?	What is rhodium?	What is ruthenium?

1 Introductory Material
Section 6

	Elements and Their Symbols X	Elements and Their Symbols XI	Elements and Their Symbols XII	Elements and Their Symbols XIII	Elements and Their Symbols XIV
5	What is Cl?	What is Mg?	What is Ne?	What is N?	What is O?
10	What is Cu?	What is Co?	What is Cr?	What is Ca?	What is Br?
15	What is Au?	What is Ir?	What is Kr?	What is Pb?	What is Pt?
20	What is W?	What is Ti?	What is Sn?	What is Se?	What is Sr?
25	What is tellurium?	What is thallium?	What is vanadium?	What is ytterbium?	What is yttrium?
B O N U S	What is promethium?	What is palladium?	What is curium?	What is actinium?	What is americium?

1 Introductory Material
Section 7

	Energy	Forms of Energy	Reaction Energy	Energy and Temperature	Heat
5	What is work?	What is chemical potential energy?	What is endothermic?	What is the Celsius scale?	What is specific heat?
10	What is kinetic energy?	What is heat, light, or radiant energy?	What is exothermic?	What is the Kelvin scale?	What is mass?
15	What is potential energy?	What is electrical energy?	What is the activation energy?	What is absolute zero?	What is quantity of heat energy?
20	What is the joule?	What is nuclear energy?	What is the joule?	What is a calorimeter?	What is change in temperature?
25	What is the law of conservation of energy?	What is mechanical energy?	What is the calorie?	What is heat energy?	What is specific heat?
BONUS	What is mechanical energy?	Many answers will apply. Electrical, chemical potential, mechanical, heat, etc.	What is a British Thermal Unit (BTU)?	What is temperature?	What is 4.18 J/g°C or 1.00 cal/g°C?

2 Atoms and Ions
Section 8

	Atomic Structure	Development of Atomic Theory	Mass and Charge	Chemists and the Atom	Models
5	What is an atom?	What is the continuous theory of matter?	What is -1?	Who is William Crookes?	What is the plum-pudding model?
10	What is an electron?	What is the discontinuous theory of matter?	What is $+1$?	Who is J.J. Thomson?	What is the Bohr model?
15	What is a proton?	What is the law of definite proportions?	What is 0 (or neutral)?	Who is Ernest Rutherford?	What is the charge-cloud model (or quantum-mechanical model)?
20	What is a neutron?	What is the law of multiple proportions?	What is 9.11×10^{-31} kg?	Who is John Dalton?	What is a model?
25	What is the nucleus?	What is the law of conservation of mass?	What is 1.67×10^{-27} kg?	Who is Robert Millikan?	What is (Heisenberg's) uncertainty principle?
BONUS	What are quarks?	Who was John Dalton?	What is 1.67×10^{-27} kg?	What is the charge/mass ratio?	What are orbitals?

2 Atoms and Ions
Section 9

	The Nature of Light	Light Energy	Atomic Measurements	Chemical Formulas I	Chemical Formulas II
5	What are quanta (or photons)?	What is frequency?	What is atomic number?	What is a chemical symbol?	What is a structural formula?
10	What is wavelength?	What is energy of an emitted photon?	What are isotopes?	What is a chemical formula?	What is qualitative analysis?
15	What is frequency?	What is Planck's constant?	What is atomic mass?	What is monatomic?	What is quantitative analysis?
20	What is velocity?	What is 6.6×10^{-34} Js (J/Hz)?	What is carbon-12?	What is diatomic?	What is CH?
25	What is a continuous spectrum?	What is the speed of light or 3.0×10^8 m/s (3.0×10^{10} cm/s)?	What is mass number?	What is a molecular formula?	What is H_2O_2?
BONUS	What are bright-line spectra?	What is lambda (or wavelength)?	What is an atomic mass unit (amu)?	What is an empirical formula?	What is a molecule?

2 Atoms and Ions
Section 10

	Oxidation Numbers/ Charges I	Oxidation Numbers/ Charges II	Oxidation Numbers/ Charges III	Oxidation Numbers/ Charges IV	Oxidation Numbers/ Charges V
5	What is 3+?	What is 2+?	What is 2+?	What is 2+?	What is 2+?
10	What is 2+?	What is 2+?	What is 1+?	What is 4+?	What is 5+?
15	What is 1+?	What is 1+?	What is 4+?	What is 2+?	What is 1+?
20	What is 2–?	What is 3–?	What is 3+?	What is 1+?	What is 1–?
25	What is 1–?	What is 1+?	What is 1–?	What is 1–?	What is 1–?
BONUS	What is 1–?	What is 1–?	What is 1–?	What is 2–?	What is 1–?

2 Atoms and Ions
Section 11

	Oxidation Numbers/ Charges VI	Oxidation Numbers/ Charges VII	Oxidation Numbers/ Charges VIII	Oxidation Numbers/ Charges IX	Oxidation Numbers/ Charges X
5	What is 3+?	What is 2+?	What is 3+?	What is 2+?	What is 2+?
10	What is 5+?	What is 4+?	What is 3+?	What is 3+?	What is 2+?
15	What is 4+?	What is 1+?	What is 1+?	What is 1+?	What is 1+?
20	What is 1–?	What is 3–?	What is 2+?	What is 3+?	What is 2+?
25	What is 2–?	What is 4–?	What is 2–?	What is 1+?	What is 2+?
BONUS	What is 2–?	What is 1–?	What is 3–?	What is 1+?	What is 2+?

2 Atoms and Ions
Section 12

	Oxidation Numbers/ Charges XI	Oxidation Numbers/ Charges XII	Oxidation Numbers/ Charges XIII	Oxidation Numbers/ Charges XIV	Oxidation Numbers/ Charges XV
5	What is 2+?	What is 2+?	What is 3+?	What is 3+?	What is 3+?
10	What is 3+?	What is 3+?	What is 2+?	What is 2+?	What is 3+?
15	What is 4+?	What is 4+?	What is 4+?	What is 4+?	What is 5+?
20	What is 1–?	What is 2+?	What is 1–?	What is 1+?	What is 1+?
25	What is 1–?	What is 1–?	What is 3–?	What is 3–?	What is 1–?
BONUS	What is 1–?	What is 1–?	What is 2–?	What is 3–?	What is 2–?

2 Atoms and Ions
Section 13

	Oxidation Numbers/ Charges XVI	Oxidation Numbers/ Charges XVII	Oxidation Numbers/ Charges XVIII	Oxidation Numbers/ Charges XIX	Oxidation Numbers/ Charges XX
5	What is 2+?	What is 3+?	What is 3+?	What is 3+?	What is 3+?
10	What is 3+?	What is 2+?	What is 4+?	What is 4+?	What is 5+?
15	What is 5+?	What is 5+?	What is 4+?	What is 4+?	What is 1+?
20	What is 2–?	What is 2–?	What is 2+?	What is 2+?	What is 1–?
25	What is 2–?	What is 1–?	What is 1–?	What is 1–?	What is 1–?
BONUS	What is 2–?	What is 2–?	What is 2–?	What is 2–?	What is 2–?

3 Compounds
Section 14

	Compounds I	Compounds II	Compounds III	The Stock System	Molecular Prefixes
5	What are metals?	What is a crystal?	What is a formula unit?	What are binary acids?	What is mono-?
10	What are nonmetals?	What is a crystal lattice?	What is a binary compound?	What are ternary acids?	What is tri-?
15	What are ions?	What is a network solid?	What is a polyatomic ion?	What is hypo-?	What is tetra-?
20	What are ionic compounds?	What are semimetals (or metalloids)?	What is a ternary compound?	What is per-?	What is hexa-?
25	What are cations?	What is an ionic compound?	What is a molecular compound?	What is 1+?	What is octa-?
BONUS	What are anions?	What is a covalent (or molecular) compound?	What is the oxidation number?	What is 7+?	What is nona-?

3 Compounds
Section 15

	Names and Formulas I	Names and Formulas II	Names and Formulas III	Names and Formulas IV	Names and Formulas V
5	What is copper (II) oxide?	What is sulfur (VI) oxide (or sulfur trioxide)?	What is aluminum oxide?	What is aluminum sulfide?	What is zinc nitride?
10	What is hydrogen chloride (or hydrochloric acid)?	What is diphosphorus triiodide?	What is iridium (IV) oxide?	What is oxygen trinitride?	What is potassium oxide?
15	What is strontium (II) cyanide?	What is beryllium hypochlorite?	What is platinum (III) phosphite?	What is beryllium chromate?	What is platinum (IV) hexafluorosilicate?
20	What is C_2S_3?	What is S_3F_6?	What is N_2O?	What is S_3S_2?	What is N_2Br_4?
25	What is $(NH_4)_2CrO_4$?	What is Na_2SO_4?	What is H_2S?	What is $LiCN$?	What is NH_4NO_3?
BONUS	What is CO?	What is SnO_2?	What is $CrBr_3$?	What is $Co_3(AsO_4)_2$?	What is Cu_2O?

3 Compounds
Section 16

	Names and Formulas VI	Names and Formulas VII	Names and Formulas VIII	Names and Formulas IX	Names and Formulas X
5	What is aluminum chloride?	What is strontium (IV) oxide?	What is aluminum fluoride?	What is sulfur dioxide?	What is beryllium bromide?
10	What is oxygen difluoride?	What is lithium iodide?	What is tetraoxygen difluoride?	What is magnesium chloride?	What is nitrogen trioxide?
15	What is calcium bromate?	What is lead (IV) phosphate?	What is calcium hydroxide?	What is nickel (III) arsenate?	What is cobalt (III) oxalate?
20	What is P_3O?	What is N_2F_4?	What is P_3O_2?	What is N_2O_3?	What is P_4O_{10}?
25	What is Na_2Se?	What is H_2O?	What is $Ba(MnO_4)_2$?	What is Li_2SO_3?	What is HCl?
BONUS	What is $GaCl_3$?	What is Ir_2O_3?	What is $Fe(CN)_3$?	What is $PbBr_2$?	What is $Mg(ClO_4)_2$?

3 Compounds
Section 17

	Names and Formulas XI	Names and Formulas XII	Names and Formulas XIII	Names and Formulas XIV	Names and Formulas XV
5	What is tin (II) sulfide?	What is carbon tetrabromide?	What is strontium (II) sulfite?	What is carbon trichloride?	What is tin (IV) oxide?
10	What is magnesium hydride?	What is nitrogen dioxide?	What is magnesium sulfide?	What is nitrogen monoxide?	What is manganese (II) chloride?
15	What is ammonium nitrite?	What is chromium (II) nitrate?	What is sodium phosphate?	What is iron (II) silicate?	What is potassium hydrogen sulfite?
20	What is N_2S_3?	What is N_4Cl_3?	What is OF_2?	What is PCl_3?	What is CO_2?
25	What is Na_2O?	What is $MgCO_3$?	What is $Be_3(AsO_4)_2$?	What is $Na_2C_2O_4$?	What is $MgCl_2$?
BONUS	What is Hg_2HPO_4?	What is NO_2?	What is PtF_2?	What is $SiCl_4$?	What is ThI_4?

3 Compounds
Section 18

	Names and Formulas XVI	Names and Formulas XVII	Names and Formulas XVIII	Names and Formulas XIX	Names and Formulas XX
5	What is carbon tetrachloride?	What is silicon diiodide?	What is carbon tetrafluoride?	What is trisulfur tetrabromide?	What is carbon monoxide?
10	What is nitrogen trichloride?	What is dinitrogen trichloride?	What is sodium sulfide?	What is sodium chloride?	What is dinitrogen pentachloride?
15	What is manganese (III) cyanide?	What is calcium hydrogen sulfate?	What is iron (III) chlorate?	What is iridium (II) acetate?	What is calcium phosphate?
20	What is NS_3?	What is N_4I?	What is CCl_4?	What is CF_4?	What is NO?
25	What is $Be(CN)_2$?	What is K_2CrO_4?	What is $Ca_3(PO_4)_2$?	What is K_3PO_4?	What is MgS?
BONUS	What is CrF_2?	What is $Co(HCO_3)_2$?	What is $Ga(ClO_3)_3$?	What is $Fe(NO_2)_3$?	What is $Pb(OH)_2$?

3 Compounds
Section 19

	Names and Formulas XXI	Names and Formulas XXII	Names and Formulas XXIII	Names and Formulas XXIV	Names and Formulas XXV
5	What is phosphorus trioxide?	What is chromium (III) bromide?	What is phosphorus pentafluoride?	What is copper (I) sulfide?	What is phosphorus pentachloride?
10	What is sodium oxide?	What is dinitrogen moniodide?	What is trinitrogen monoxide?	What is dinitrogen monoxide?	What is trinitrogen tetraiodide?
15	What is magnesium carbonate?	What is lithium carbonate?	What is sodium sulfate?	What is sodium bromate?	What is nickel (II) carbonate?
20	What is SO_2?	What is CO_3?	What is ON_3?	What is PCl_5?	What is NI_3?
25	What is Na_2SiF_6?	What is $Ca_3(PO_3)_2$?	What is K_2SiO_3?	What is $CaSiO_3$?	What is Rb_2SO_4?
B O N U S	What is $Hg_2(CN)_2$?	What is N_2O_5?	What is SO_3?	What is $Cr_2(C_2O_4)_3$?	What is CdO_2?

3 Compounds
Section 20

	Names and Formulas XXVI	Names and Formulas XXVII	Names and Formulas XXVIII	Names and Formulas XXIX	Names and Formulas XXX
5	What is copper (II) nitride?	What is phosphorus trichloride?	What is copper (II) iodide?	What is lead (IV) oxide?	What is gallium (III) oxide?
10	What is dinitrogen trioxide?	What is dinitrogen pentoxide?	What is dinitrogen trisulfide?	What is silver oxalate?	What is zinc hydroxide?
15	What is mercury (I) cyanide?	What is nickel (II) cyanide?	What is cobalt (II) hexafluorosilicate?	What is mercury (I) phosphide?	What is gallium (I) hydrogen sulfate?
20	What is S_2Br_5?	What is O_2Cl_5?	What is PCl_4?	What is O_2Cl_3?	What is AlI_3?
25	What is $CaC_4H_4O_6$?	What is MgI_2?	What is $CsClO$?	What is $Al_2(CO_3)_3$?	What is $IrPO_4$?
B O N U S	What is $CuHSO_4$?	What is $Fe(C_2H_3O_2)_3$?	What is PbO_2?	What is $NiCO_3$?	What is $Pt(NO_2)_2$?

3 Compounds
Section 21

	Names and Formulas XXXI	Names and Formulas XXXII	Names and Formulas XXXIII	Names and Formulas XXXIV	Names and Formulas XXXV
5	What is lead (II) oxide?	What is hydrogen sulfide?	What is tetraphosphorus decoxide?	What is hydrogen bromide?	What is diphosphorus pentoxide?
10	What is aluminum permanganate?	What is thorium (III) arsenate?	What is aluminum dichromate?	What is thorium (IV) hydrogen carbonate?	What is barium nitrate?
15	What is iron (II) tartrate?	What is chromium (III) carbonate?	What is copper (I) hydrogen carbonate?	What is cobalt (II) acetate?	What is chromium (III) chlorite?
20	What is $SrSiF_6$?	What is Li_2CO_3?	What is NH_4ClO_3?	What is Na_2S?	What is HBr?
25	What is $AlCl_3$?	What is $Sn(SO_3)_2$?	What is $CoCr_2O_7$?	What is $Sr_3(PO_4)_2$?	What is $Zn(OH)_2$?
B O N U S	What is ThO_2?	What is Cr_2O_3?	What is Cu_2S?	What is Fe_2O_3?	What is PbO?

4 Reactions and Gas Laws
Section 22

	Stoichiometry	Mole Relationships I	Mole Relationships II	Mole Relationships III	Mole Relationships IV
5	What is formula mass?	What is 12.0 g?	What is 32 g?	What is 23.0 g?	What is 55.8 g?
10	What is molecular mass?	What is 1.8 moles?	What is 1.5 moles?	What is 4.3 moles?	What is 6.27 moles?
15	What is the gram atomic mass?	What is 44.8 L or dm^3?	What is 108 L or dm^3?	What is 36 L or dm^3?	What is 2.0 L or dm^3?
20	What is the gram formula mass?	What is 8.4×10^{23} atoms?	What is 1.2×10^{24} atoms?	What is 4×10^{24} atoms?	What is 2×10^{21} atoms?
25	What is the gram molecular mass?	What is 14 L or dm^3?	What is 120 L or dm^3?	What is 31 L or dm^3?	What is 49 L or dm^3?
B O N U S	What is 6.02×10^{23} particles?	What is 8.5×10^{23} atoms?	What is 2.6×10^{23} atoms?	What is 1.95×10^{24} atoms?	What is 3.95×10^{23} atoms?

4 Reactions and Gas Laws
Section 23

	Mole Relationships V	Mole Relationships VI	Mole Relationships VII	Mole Relationships VIII	Mole Relationships IX
5	What is 40.1 g?	What is 2.0 g?	What is 63.5 g?	What is 159.8 g?	What is 207.2 g?
10	What is 1.46 moles?	What is 17 moles?	What is 4.16 moles?	What is 5.77 moles?	What is 0.17 moles?
15	What is 49.5 L or dm^3?	What is 87 L or dm^3?	What is 5.11 L or dm^3?	What is 2.7 L or dm^3?	What is 0.0502 L or dm^3?
20	What is 2×10^{21} atoms?	What is 1.8×10^4 atoms?	What is 14 atoms?	What is 1.3×10^{24} atoms?	What is 60 atoms?
25	What is 32.1 L or dm^3?	What is 5.2×10^1 L or dm^3?	What is 253 L or dm^3?	What is 740 L or dm^3?	What is 860 L or dm^3?
BONUS	What is 3.63×10^{23} atoms?	What is 5.72×10^{24} atoms?	What is 1.0×10^{22} atoms?	What is 3 atoms?	What is 4 atoms?

4 Reactions and Gas Laws
Section 24

	Chemical Equations	Chemical Reactions	Balanced Equation Relationships	Phases and Pressure	Phases and Temperature
5	What are reactants?	What is combination (or synthesis)?	What is Avogadro's hypothesis?	What is pressure?	What is the boiling point?
10	What are products?	What is decomposition (or analysis)?	What is one molar volume (or 22.4 dm^3 or L)?	What is atmospheric (or air) pressure?	What is the condensation point?
15	What is a catalyst?	What is single replacement?	What is a mass-mass problem?	What is 0°C (or 273 K)?	What is the melting point?
20	What is a coefficient?	What is double replacement?	What are excess reactants?	What is 760 mmHg (or 101.3 kPa)?	What is the freezing point?
25	What is balancing an equation?	What is a precipitate?	What is the limiting reactant (reagent)?	What is 1 000?	What is evaporation?
BONUS	What is an exothermic reaction?	What is combustion?	What is a volume-volume problem?	What is a newton per meter squared?	What is condensation?

4 Reactions and Gas Laws
Section 25

	Kinetic Theory	Phase Changes I	Phase Changes II	Phase Changes III	Potpourri
5	What is a molecule?	What is vapor pressure?	What is distillation (or fractionation)?	What is hygroscopic?	What is 100?
10	What is constant, random motion?	What is liquefaction?	What is sublimation?	What is anhydrous?	What is a compound?
15	What is elastic?	What is the heat of vaporization?	What is a hydrate?	What is the water of hydration (or water of crystallization)?	What is the kelvin?
20	What is none?	What is the heat of fusion?	What is decrepitation?	What is viscosity?	What is the mass number?
25	What is kinetic energy?	What is the heat of crystallization?	What is efflorescence?	What is high viscosity?	What is $CaCl_2$?
B O N U S	What is temperature?	What is the heat of condensation?	What is deliquescence?	What is a density decrease?	What is 2–?

4 Reactions and Gas Laws
Section 26

	Boyle's Law	Charles's Law	Gay-Lussac's Law	The Combined Gas Law	The Ideal Gas Law
5	What is $PV = K$ (or $P_1V_1 = P_2V_2$)?	What is $V/T = K$ (or $V_1/T_1 = V_2/T_2$)?	What is $P/T = K$ (or $P_1/T_1 = P_2/T_2$)?	What is $PV/T = K$ (or $P_1V_1/T_1 = P_2V_2/T_2$)?	What is $PV = nRT$?
10	What is pressure?	What is temperature?	What is $P_2 = P_1T_2/T_1$?	What is $P_2 = P_1V_1T_2/T_1V_2$?	What is the number of moles of gas?
15	What is volume?	What is $T_2 = V_2T_1/V_1$?	What is $T_2 = T_1P_2/P_1$?	What is $V_2 = P_1V_1T_2/T_1P_2$?	What is the ideal gas law constant?
20	What is $P_2 = P_1V_1/V_2$?	What is $V_2 = V_1T_2/T_1$?	What is double P_1?	What is $T_2 = P_2V_2T_1/P_1V_1$?	What is $P = nRT/V$?
25	What is half of V_1?	What is twice T_1?	What is half of P_1?	What is Charles's law?	What is $T = PV/nR$?
B O N U S	What is twice V_1?	What is half T_1?	What is double T_2?	What is Boyle's law?	What is $n = PV/RT$?

5 The Periodic Nature of Chemistry
Section 27

	Atomic Structure and Electron Configurations I	Atomic Structure and Electron Configurations II	Electron Configurations	Periodic Table I	Periodic Quantities
5	What is the principal quantum number?	What is the excited state?	What is hydrogen?	What are the groups (or families)?	What are atomic numbers?
10	What is a sublevel (or subshell)?	What is hybridization?	What is carbon?	What are the periods?	What is atomic mass?
15	What is an orbital?	What is the Pauli exclusion principle?	What is neon?	What are the metals?	What is the atomic name?
20	What are s, p, d, and f?	What are valence electrons?	What is sodium?	What are the nonmetals?	What is a chemical symbol?
25	What are 2, 6, 10, 14?	What is 8?	What is chlorine?	What are the semimetals or metalloids?	What is an electron configuration?
BONUS	What is spherical?	What are transfer and sharing of electrons?	What is krypton?	What are transuranium or transuranic elements?	What are oxidation numbers or charges?

5 The Periodic Nature of Chemistry
Section 28

	Periodic Table II	Group 1	Group 2	Group 17	Group 18
5	What are the alkali metals?	What is H?	What is Be?	What is F?	What is He?
10	What are the alkaline earth metals?	What is Li?	What is Mg?	What is Cl?	What is Ne?
15	What are the noble gases?	What is Na?	What is Ca?	What is Br?	What is Ar?
20	What are the halogens?	What is potassium?	What is strontium?	What is iodine?	What is krypton?
25	What is the oxygen family (or the chalcogens)?	What is rubidium?	What is barium?	What is astatine?	What is xenon?
BONUS	What is the carbon family?	What is cesium?	What is radium?	What are the halogens?	What is radon?

5 The Periodic Nature of Chemistry
Section 29

	Groups 13–14	Groups 15–16	Transition Elements I	Transition Elements II	Inner Transition Elements
5	What is aluminum?	What is bismuth?	What is iron?	What is mercury?	What is einsteinium?
10	What is carbon?	What is tellurium?	What is copper?	What is cadmium?	What is americium?
15	What is lead?	What is polonium?	What is tungsten?	What is gold?	What is uranium?
20	What is tin?	What is nitrogen?	What is silver?	What is nickel?	What is plutonium?
25	What is boron?	What is oxygen?	What is platinum?	What is titanium?	What is curium?
BONUS	What is silicon?	What is phosphorus?	What is chromium?	What is zinc?	What is californium?

5 The Periodic Nature of Chemistry
Section 30

	Periodicity	Bonding	Other Bonds	VSEPR	Other Bond Behaviors
5	What is ionization energy?	What is a chemical bond?	What is a covalent bond?	What is Valence-Shell Electron-Pair Repulsion?	What is resonance?
10	What is electronegativity?	What is an ionic bond?	What is a molecular substance?	What is linear?	What are polar molecules?
15	What is atomic radius?	What is a stable octet?	What is a binary molecule?	What is bent?	What are nonpolar molecules?
20	What is ionic radius?	What is a dot diagram (or a Lewis structure)?	What is a coordinate covalent bond?	What is trigonal planar?	What are van der Waals forces?
25	What is shielding effect?	What are the kernel electrons (or inner-shell electrons)?	What is a double bond?	What is pyramidal?	What is hydrogen bond?
BONUS	What is periodic law?	What are electrovalent bonds?	What is a triple bond?	What is tetrahedral?	What is a dipole?

6 Solutions, Kinetics, and Acids and Bases
Section 31

	Solutions I	Solutions II	Concentration I	Concentration II	Colligative Properties
5	What is a heterogeneous mixture?	What are miscible?	What is saturated?	What is molarity?	What is an electrolyte?
10	What is a homogeneous mixture?	What are immiscible?	What is unsaturated?	What is molality?	What is freezing point depression?
15	What is the solute?	What is an alloy?	What is supersaturated?	What is 1.1 M?	What is boiling point elevation?
20	What is the solvent?	What is an amalgam?	What is concentrated?	What is 2.2 m?	What is the freezing point elevation constant?
25	What is an aqueous solution?	What is solubility?	What is dilute?	What is 1 mole?	What is the boiling point elevation constant?
BONUS	What is a tincture?	What is a solubility curve?	What is solution equilibrium?	What is 6 moles?	What is molality?

6 Solutions, Kinetics, and Acids and Bases
Section 32

	Kinetics I	Kinetics II	Kinetics III	Equilibrium	Acids and Bases I
5	What is reaction rate?	What is a catalyst?	What is the rate-determining step?	What is a reversible reaction?	What are electrolytes?
10	What is the mechanism?	What is Le Chatelier's principle?	What is enthalpy?	What is chemical equilibrium?	What are nonelectrolytes?
15	What is an effective collision?	What is a precipitate?	What is the heat of reaction?	What is physical equilibrium?	What are strong electrolytes?
20	What is a homogeneous reaction?	What is a spectator ion?	What is the heat of formation?	What is chemical equilibrium?	What are weak electrolytes?
25	What is a heterogeneous reaction?	What is an activated complex?	What is entropy?	What is the equilibrium constant?	What is dissociation?
BONUS	What is surface area?	What is the activation energy?	What is the change in free energy?	What are the molar concentrations of reactants and products?	What is ionization (or ionic dissociation)?

6 | Solutions, Kinetics, and Acids and Bases
Section 33

	Acids and Bases II	Acids and Bases III	Acids and Bases IV	Acids and Bases V	Acid or Base?
5	What is hydronium?	What are bases?	What is a salt?	What is self-ionization?	What is an acid?
10	What is an Arrhenius acid?	What are acids?	What is neutralization?	What is pH?	What is a base?
15	What is the ionization constant?	What is sour?	What is a proton?	What is a buffer?	What is a base?
20	What is water?	What is bitter?	What is a proton?	What is an indicator?	What is an acid?
25	What is hydrogen?	What are electrolytes?	What is hydrolysis?	What is titration?	What is an acid?
BONUS	What is red?	What is blue?	What is an ampholyte (or an amphoteric or amphiprotic substance)?	What is the equivalence point?	What is a base?

7 | Electrochemistry, Organic Chemistry, Biochemistry, and Nuclear Chemistry
Section 34

	Redox Reactions	Electrochemistry	Organic Chemistry I	Organic Chemistry II	Organic Chemistry III
5	What is oxidation?	What is the cathode?	What are isomers?	What is saturated?	What are the aromatic hydrocarbons?
10	What is reduction?	What is the anode?	What are hydrocarbons?	What is unsaturated?	What are the paraffins?
15	What is the oxidation number?	What is an electrolyte?	What are straight-chain hydrocarbons?	What are alkanes?	What is an alkyl group?
20	What is the oxidizing agent?	What is brine?	What are branched-chain hydrocarbons?	What is an alkene?	What is benzene?
25	What is the reducing agent?	What is electroplating?	What is a cyclic hydrocarbon?	What is an alkyne?	What is substitution?
BONUS	What are half reactions?	What is electrolysis?	What is aliphatic?	What is an alkadiene?	What is polymerization?

7 Electrochemistry, Organic Chemistry, Biochemistry, and Nuclear Chemistry
Section 35

	Organic Chemistry IV	Organic Chemistry V	Organic Chemistry VI	Biochemistry I	Biochemistry II
5	What is a polymer?	What are the ketones?	What is a primary alcohol?	What is biochemistry?	What are the nucleic acids?
10	What is a monomer?	What are carboxylic acids?	What is a secondary alcohol?	What are the carbohydrates?	What is ribonucleic acid?
15	What is an alcohol?	What is fractional distillation?	What is a tertiary alcohol?	What are the lipids?	What is deoxyribonucleic acid?
20	What is hydroxyl?	What is cracking?	What are detergents?	What are the proteins?	What is an enzyme?
25	What is an ether?	What is a dihydroxy alcohol?	What is hard water?	What are amino acids?	What is a substrate?
BONUS	What is an aldehyde?	What is an ester?	What is saponification?	What is a peptide bond?	What are nucleotides?

7 Electrochemistry, Organic Chemistry, Biochemistry, and Nuclear Chemistry
Section 36

	Nuclear Chemistry I	Nuclear Chemistry II	Nuclear Chemistry III	Nuclear Chemistry IV	Nuclear Chemistry V
5	What are alpha particles?	What is alpha emission?	What is uranium (or plutonium)?	What is a linear accelerator?	What is $E = mc^2$?
10	What are beta particles?	What is beta emission?	What is a tracer?	What is a synchrotron?	What are the transuranic (or transuranium) elements?
15	What is gamma radiation?	What is gamma emission?	What is nuclear medicine (or radiology)?	What is nuclear fission?	What is critical mass?
20	What is half-life?	What is a positron?	What is radioactive dating?	What is nuclear fusion?	What is a control rod?
25	What are nuclides?	What is an antiparticle?	What is a particle accelerator?	What is a chain reaction?	What is the rem?
BONUS	What is a radioisotope?	What is antimatter?	What is a cyclotron?	What is a moderator (or control rod)?	What is transmutation?

Share Your Bright Ideas

We want to hear from you!

Your name_____Date_____

School name_____

School address_____

City _____State _____Zip_____Phone number (_____)_____

Grade level(s) taught_____Subject area(s) taught_____

Where did you purchase this publication?_____

In what month do you purchase a majority of your supplements?_____

What moneys were used to purchase this product?

____School supplemental budget   ____Federal/state funding   ____Personal

Please "grade" this Walch publication in the following areas:

Quality of service you received when purchasing ....A   B   C   D

Ease of use...A   B   C   D

Quality of content..A   B   C   D

Page layout ....A   B   C   D

Organization of material ....A   B   C   D

Suitability for grade level..A   B   C   D

Instructional value...A   B   C   D

COMMENTS:_____

_____

What specific supplemental materials would help you meet your current—or future—instructional needs?

_____

Have you used other Walch publications? If so, which ones?_____

May we use your comments in upcoming communications?   ____Yes   ____No

Please **FAX** this completed form to **888-991-5755**, or mail it to

Customer Service, Walch Publishing, P. O. Box 658, Portland, ME 04104-0658

We will send you a **FREE GIFT** in appreciation of your feedback. **THANK YOU!**